The Swedish Nightingale: Jenny Lind

Books for Young People
by Elisabeth Kyle
THE SWEDISH NIGHTINGALE:
JENNY LIND
GIRL WITH A PEN:
CHARLOTTE BRONTË

The Swedish Nightingale: Jenny Lind

BY ELISABETH KYLE

HOLT, RINEHART AND WINSTON

NEW YORK CHICAGO SAN FRANCISCO

For the Leigh Cooks,
with my love

The Swedish Nightingale: Jenny Lind

Entr'acte

"They say she has no ears."

The woman clinging to her husband's arm had wanted to whisper the words. But she had to shout them instead because of the noise of the crowd. It was eleven o'clock at night, on Sunday, September 1, 1850. New York's Broadway, still a handsome residential quarter, should have been settling down. Instead, twenty thousand people were milling about under the windows of the quiet Irving House Hotel.

Somebody heard what she said. An indignant voice shouted back: "No ears, Ma'am? Stuff and nonsense!"

The woman twisted around and called back indignantly, "Who's seen them? Why does she wear her hair in those loops? In all the pictures——"

"Hush, my love!" Her embarrassed husband squeezed her more tightly to his side. He added, into her own ear, "This crowd's no place for you. You should have stayed home."

"What, and miss seeing her? You know very well——"

A movement among the crowd cut her short. All heads had been turned toward the iron balcony jutting out from a first-floor window of the hotel. Now they were turned the other way. There was the sound of a band coming along the street. The yellow gas lamps along Broadway seemed to flicker and pale. Yet the light grew stronger, but it was red. It came now from a line of torches wavering from the distance toward the hotel.

"Make way there!"

"Stand back!"

Shouting and cheers. The tightly wedged thousands distributed themselves somehow, trickling like streams of water toward the other side of the road. Those in front gasped at the magnificence of the approaching procession. First came the band. Then twenty brigades of New York Firemen wearing red shirts and carrying torches. And, surrounded and protected by this body-guard, two hundred self-conscious people stepping along as best they might; the members of the New York Musical Fund Society.

They drew up under the empty balcony. The body-guard made a semicircle about them, holding their torches high. The torchlight turned the red shirts of their bearers black, then played over the bonnets and hats of the crowd. There was a breathless hush. Now most people could see that the dark square of glass beyond the balcony was lit up, too. Somebody had drawn a curtain aside. Somebody was unlatching the window, which opened onto the balcony like a door.

She was coming out at last. . . .

She was dressed in white. The crowd could hardly make out her face. She shrank, too, as a square, thickset figure almost dragged her forward. The crowd knew that figure all right. It was Phineas Barnum, the great showman.

Although this was a hot, close night, Barnum wore his usual fur-collared overcoat. They would scarcely have known him without it. He had his glossy top hat in his hand, too, and he rested it on the rail of the balcony as he shouted down to the crowd.

"Ladies and Gentlemen! You know me. Phineas Barnum. I have brought world-famous novelties before you, time and again. I now bring to you the greatest of them all——" He paused, while the shrinking figure beside him half-turned as if wanting to fly back through the glass door again. "I present to you tonight, Madame Jenny Lind, The Swedish Nightingale."

A roar of applause shattered the momentary silence. It echoed right down Broadway. It came again and again. The members of the Musical Society, who had stepped forward to begin their serenade, could not open their mouths. They stood, embarrassed, clapping their hands, while the white figure on the balcony dipped in a shy, stiff curtsey.

After a few seconds, Barnum held up his hand. Scarcely anyone else in New York could have commanded silence at such a moment. But the great showman could handle crowds as nobody else could. There was silence at once.

He signaled toward the band which, with the choir, burst into *Hail Columbia*. The crowd took it up, and the roar of voices seemed to overwhelm the white figure on the balcony. She flinched for a moment, then came forward resolutely, waving her hands in thanks. The band switched to *Yankee Doodle*, and this too was bellowed by the enthusiastic crowd, so that the trained voices of the Musical Society were swamped and all their painstaking practice went for nothing.

9

Again the white figure curtseyed; waved to the crowd in thanks, then turned resolutely toward the window and passed through it out of sight. Phineas Barnum made a flamboyant gesture with his hat, and stepped through it after her. The balcony was empty again.

The crowd slowly dispersed. There were few women here at this time of night, but there were some, and respectable matrons, too. The one who had spoken about Jenny's ears turned triumphantly toward her husband.

"There you are! Only a great bunch of hair on each side of her face. I'll warrant they conceal some deformity! And no jewelry neither. Just a bracelet on one arm."

"Then what did you badger me to bring you out for? Did you think she was one of Barnum's Freaks?" the exasperated husband demanded.

"She's nothing to look at anyway."

"Our European correspondent heard her somewhere in Germany. Said she looks lovely on the stage. Real lovely."

"Get along with you! That Swedish pudding face couldn't look anything."

"Maybe when she sings——"

"Yes, maybe."

Curiously enough, Phineas Barnum was thinking the same thing, as he stood opposite his latest find in the private sitting room reserved for her in the hotel. A homely-looking woman, he was saying to himself. But though nowadays it took a good deal to surprise him, he felt once more the surprise he had known when he first

10

heard her sing. That such a dull, plain face could so transform itself on the stage! When she sang Norma for instance, she didn't just sing the music; she *was* Norma; or La Sonnambula, or the Daughter of the Regiment.

Or anything you like.

And, by some magic which even he could not explain, she became beautiful, too.

But now she was far from beautiful. She was a tired, plain woman, still exhausted by the sea voyage from England, and the tumultuous welcome in New York harbor, the beflagged tugboats, the speeches and bouquets and triumphal arches under which she had, just a few hours before, driven to this hotel.

Could he, had he, made a mistake?

He looked at her simple dress and frowned. "I asked you, Madame, to wear all your jewels, or as many as possible anyway. It is well known that you have received a fortune in diamonds from enthusiastic admirers. Why not have given the crowd the pleasure of seeing 'em?"

A magnificent bouquet—his bouquet—lay on a little marble-topped table. She sat down wearily beside it. "It is my voice which interests the people. Not my jewels. I hate jewels."

His eye fell on the one piece she wore; a heavy gold bracelet set with pearls. "Things like that don't catch the light. Don't sparkle."

For the first time a look of amusement crossed her face. "Not even if it was given me by Queen Victoria?"

"You don't say!" He looked at it with more interest. "And she'll have paid you a hearty compliment, too. Everyone knows the Queen worships your singing."

11

Jenny twisted the bracelet around. "She said——"
Then she paused.

"Well, Madame? What did she say?"

"I'm afraid I am boastful in repeating it. But I value her compliment more than any I have ever received. She herself clasped the bracelet on my arm and said, 'I give you this with my respect as well as my admiration.' "

He drew a deep breath. "That was something, coming from *her!*"

Jenny stood up, unclasping the bracelet as she spoke. "I am very tired. Now that I have made a spectacle of myself, will you excuse me?"

He jumped to his feet. "Of course! I wouldn't have you tired out for the world. Not with your first concert coming on. Have you settled the programme by the way?"

"Certainly. I shall begin with the song *Casta Diva* from *Norma*. Then the trio with two flutes from Meyerbeer's *Camp of Silesia*. And I'll end, as usual, with a group of our own Swedish national songs."

"Trio with two flutes! That'll fetch 'em." He hesitated. "But the Swedish songs, Madame? They'll be simple things, I suppose. No runs and trills. Our folk don't understand Swedish neither. Or Italian for that matter. But Italian's fashionable all the same——"

"While Swedish isn't? I always sing some of our own music at *all* my concerts, Mr. Barnum. You see, I am a simple person myself, too."

"As you like, of course." He began to walk toward the door, but turned with the knob in his hand to look anxiously back at her. "We're auctioning the tickets.

12

Get more for 'em that way. Why, there's one business acquaintance of mine says he's willing to bid up to three hundred dollars for his! And my wife's maid has put aside half of her whole month's wages to buy a ticket. Twenty dollars she's put aside——"

Jenny stepped with a quick movement toward a velvet bag lying on the table beside the flowers. Plunging her hand into it she pulled out a handful of notes. "Please give the girl back her twenty dollars, and see that she gets a seat."

"Why, that's a fine action!" His mind was already busy, as he counted the notes, with how to phrase this generous gift for the newspapers next morning. "They told me, over in Europe, you gave the money away that you earned, right and left——"

"That is why I trouble to earn it. And now, if you will excuse me——"

"By all means. Got to save your voice. Sweet sleep, tired nature's something-or-other. You don't think the sea voyage has done anything to the vocal chords, eh?"

She looked at him with something like contempt. "Do you want to hear it?" Throwing her head back, she let a pure volume of sound fill the room:

"Casta Divá, che inargenti,
 Queste sacre, queste sacra antiche piante——"

The notes fell, liquid as water, sung *mezzo voce*, yet clear as a bird's. He listened, enchanted, head on one side. When she had finished the phrase from the Italian aria, she held out her hand decisively. "Have no fear

13

about the concert, sir. I shall easily win back the money you have spent upon me—and more."

When he had gone, she walked slowly through the folding doors into her bedroom beyond. Her maid, Selma, a woman of about the same age as herself, rose sleepily, yawning, from an armchair beside the bed. Through the half-open window a clock struck midnight.

"You are exhausted, Madame. Sit down and let me brush your hair. That always restores you."

They spoke in Swedish together. She unhooked the bodice of Jenny's dress, slipped a cool muslin peignoir over her shoulders, and began to take down her hair. The glossy loops were straightened out, revealing two ears like anyone else's. When her hair was plaited, the maid said, "Your flowers, Madame. Your bouquet! I must put them in water. Shall I bring them in here?"

Jenny shook her head. "They are too heavily scented. I would barter them gladly for a handful of our Swedish anemones. *Those* you could have brought in here. To remind me of home."

"Homesick again, Jenny?" The woman's voice was gentle. She had forgotten to call her Madame. And why not? Had they not played together as children?

"Always homesick. You know that."

"I heard you trying your voice."

"Mr. Barnum wanted to hear if his investment was equal to paying dividends," her mistress said drily. "He was cross with me, too, for not putting on more jewelry. Yet he calls me the Swedish Nightingale. Doesn't he know that the peacock, not the nightingale, has the best plumage? And think of the peacock's voice!"

14

The candles flickered on either side of the mirror. Jenny leaned forward, studying her face. Then her lips parted. She began to sing again, softly:

> *"Where the birch tree bends to the water,*
> *It trembles and looks at its shade,*
> *'Who am I, to stand proudly for ever?*
> *I am only what God has made.'"*

Selma laid down the hairbrush. "I've heard that song in Sweden. You never sang it before."

"I heard a peasant sing it once, long ago. When I was a child in Sollentuna. I thought I'd forgotten it. The thought of our anemones and nightingales brought it suddenly back."

"In Sollentuna?" The maid shook her head. "I must have heard it there too."

Jenny walked over to the ornate bed with its crochet cover flung back. She slipped wearily between the sheets. "Please give me my little clock to wind."

The clock was really a pendant watch. Selma handed it to her mistress. It was a fragile thing made of gold, with a little gold crown in diamonds above the face, and a scrolled letter D under the crown.

"My first present from royalty!" Jenny murmured as she wound it. "Our Queen said it would always tell me when the time came for me to return to Sweden. But it hasn't yet."

Selma moved through the room now, blowing out the candles. Presently she placed a nightlight in a glass shade by the bedside table. Her mistress hated going to sleep in the dark. But when she was about to light it, Jenny stopped her.

"Not tonight, Selma dear. I want it to be dark to-night. Quite dark. Then I can think I am back in Sweden."

The door closed behind Selma. The room was quite dark. Faint sounds from a city half-asleep came through the open window. One could imagine they were the wind in the birch trees lining the lake near Sollentuna. Jenny lay on her back in the darkness, trying to forget the hotel furniture about her; trying to see, once more, the carpet of anemones nodding under the Swedish birches in spring.

Beside her, Queen Desideria's watch ticked away softly. Like the heart of Sweden itself.

CHAPTER I

It was the summer of 1824, when this story really began.

The Ferndal's house in Sollentuna stood right beside the ancient church. This was natural, since Carl Ferndal was its sacristan. The house was a good one, built solidly of wood and painted the color of ox-blood. The color showed up warmly against the little wood of silver birches just behind the house.

Carl Ferndal and his wife had come from Finland and settled here, long ago. The people of Sollentuna still laughed a little at their funny accent and ways. It was even whispered that Fru Ferndal's mother had been a witch! Everyone knew that in the quiet, ghostly stretches of Finland witches still lived. What else could you expect, in a land where peoples' wealth was counted in reindeer instead of money, and where, in summer, the sun never sank?

People were sorry for the Ferndals, because they had no children. Fortunately they had been given a little girl to bring up. There was gossip about her when she had first arrived as a baby. An unwanted child, it seemed. Boarded out in the country on that account. Still, it was, at least, a child in the house. And no fault of the Ferndals that the child was so plain.

When asked, she could stumble out her full name. Johanna Maria Lind. But nobody called her anything except Jenny. She was a fat, square child with a thatch of fair hair, a snub nose and a very wide mouth. She wasn't very interesting either. There was only one odd thing about her. When the choir met to practice the old Swedish church music, you couldn't keep her away from the church. She would slip inside and sit quiet as a mouse. And once, when the leading soprano sang a wrong note, Jenny corrected her, piping the whole phrase in a little, pure voice. This made the soprano angry. She said children about the place put her off. Jenny was led firmly out.

"But she sang a wrong note!" She protested to Carl Ferndal at supper that night.

"Little bats mustn't squeak," he told her. When she had got down from her chair and trotted out of the room, he turned to his wife and said, "The choirmaster says she has perfect pitch. Really, what an ear for a child!"

Jenny was four that summer. Although this wasn't Finland, still, the sun took its time about sinking here, too. Midday stretched right into evening, and still it blazed down on the green meadows, the birch wood, the glinting arm of the lake. It threw itself against the whiteness of the bell tower which, like most bell towers in Sweden, stood a little apart from the church. And hardly had it sunk at last, when it rose up again, at two or three in the morning.

This made it difficult for Jenny to sleep. She had a little room up in the rafters, smelling of warm pine logs. Downstairs, the house smelled of pine trees, too, because in summer the floors were covered with branches of fresh pine to keep dusty shoes from soiling their whiteness. Jenny slept in a small bunk bed with a coverlet of eiderduck feathers over her. One of Fru Ferndal's home-spun sheets was buttoned onto its underside, so however much she wriggled, the coverlet always kept smooth. There was a tiny window between two beams. Fru Ferndal had tacked a curtain across it. But the sun shone so strongly through the thin stuff, and the birds sang so loudly outside, Jenny woke up this morning although it was not yet five.

She lay and listened. Through the birdsong came the steady tick-tack of the painted clock downstairs. She could hear Father Ferndal snoring, too. Outside, the morning would be clear and fresh. A pity to waste it. She got up very softly, pulled on her clothes, not bother-ing about the buttons up the back, and crept barefoot downstairs.

The big wooden bolt to the front door was hard to pull back. She had to take two hands to it. But when she slipped through at last, everything looked bathed in clear magic. The flowers, wet with dew, brushed her little legs as she went through the garden, then out onto the road.

She wasn't allowed out on the road alone. Not with-out Selma. Selma was a big girl of six, and sensible enough not to take her too far or let her fall into the lake. There was Selma, already feeding the chickens out-side her house! She was throwing the grain out from her checked apron. Jenny waited until she had finished. Then the two began walking along the road together.

"Did you hear the noise our hens made?" Selma asked. "It's the sun that wakens them so early. Mother heard me moving, so she said I could give them some grain to keep them quiet."

"Nobody knows I'm out," said Jenny with satisfaction.

They left the road and entered a meadow. The cows, still on their knees, watched them pass. "Won't your mother be angry?" asked Selma, meaning Fru Ferndal, for that was the only mother that Jenny knew.

"She's never angry," Jenny answered, adding doubtfully, "except when she has her pain."

Selma looked sorry. Everybody in Sollentuna knew about the new, queer pain in Fru Ferndal's breast, and the wiser ones shook their heads. It was a serious symptom, they said. Soon, they said, the child may become neglected; for who can attend to their duties with a pain like that?

Jenny was speaking again. "She never tells me stories any more. She says she's too tired."

"What kind of stories?"

"Well—about people being turned into wolves. They can do that in Finland. There was once a man"—Jenny began to speak very rapidly, clutching Selma's hand as she spoke—"and he was a bad man. So they turned him into a wolf. He ran around and around like a dog and ate raw meat. Then he got good so they turned him back. But, do you know——"

"What?" Selma looked cautiously over her shoulder. The meadow was still peaceful, and there were the cows.

"For *all his life long* he had a tail. And he had a big, sharp claw on one hand!"

"I suppose he tucked his tail into his trousers." Selma

was practical. "And I don't believe that story anyway," she finished.

"She tells me about the Trolls. They live in the mountains but I don't mind *them*. There aren't any mountains in this part of Sweden."

"Oh, Trolls! I know about them, too. They've got big heads and they work mischief. Look here, Jenny"—she dropped her voice suddenly—"does Fru Ferndal ever tell you about—witches?"

"Witches? What are they?" The round face with the snub nose looked up inquiringly into Selma's.

"They can work spells. And they can tell what's going to happen. I've heard it said"—she dropped her voice still further—"that Fru Ferndal's own mother was a witch!"

"Witches! Witches! Witches!" Jenny ran through the long grass, chanting the new word. She was too small to be frightened. It was just another name, like Troll, or Werewolf. Selma ran after her. The blue flowers in the meadow bent and rustled as they passed. And now, they were coming to the lake.

Before they quite reached it, they heard somebody singing. It was the maidservant from the Pastor's house, and already she was washing the clothes. She was kneeling by the side of the water, with one of the Pastor's shirts laid out on a stone, and she was pounding it with another stone, splashing the water from the clear blue lake over the shirt from time to time. They were near enough now to hear the words that she sang:

"Where the birch tree bends to the water,

21

It trembles and looks at its shade.
'Who am I, to stand proudly for ever?
I am only what God has made.' "

It was a simple tune, with a curious melancholy air.
Jenny stood listening to it, entranced. "That's a new
tune," she said.

The girl laughed. "Indeed, and it is an old, old one.
My grandmother used to sing it to me, but she had forgotten most of the words. You're a naughty girl, Jenny.
What are you doing so far from home at this hour in the
morning?"

"What are *you* doing?" answered the child pertly.

"Fru Pastor's not one to let a body sleep on a day like
this! She likes the clothes washed before breakfast."

"Breakfast?" Jenny licked her lips. "I'm hungry.
C'me on, Selma, let's go home again."

When they entered the village, there was a small
hubbub around the Inn. The post chaise from Stockholm stood there, but the postman had gone inside for
his breakfast, too. He must have dealt out the letters, for
people stood reading them there in the street, though
some were already hurrying home to enjoy them in
peace.

Jenny said good-by to Selma and trotted cautiously
into the house. She couldn't pretend she had only just
risen, because there were Papa and Mama Ferndal sitting at table already, and they must have missed her a
good while ago. But strangely enough, they paid her no
attention at all. Mama Ferndal's face was drawn and
white as it often was, nowadays, after a sleepless night.

22

Carl Ferndal pushed a bowl of porridge over to her, and then reread the open letter on the table before him.

"She might have let us keep her a little longer," he said to his wife, adding in spite of her warning glance toward the child. "After all, you only wrote last week to tell her about your health."

"Say nothing before the child. What is best done, is best done quickly," she replied. "Let her enjoy her breakfast in peace."

Jenny's large mouth withdrew itself from the porridge spoon. She was just going to ask a question, when Papa Ferndal dropped a large knob of butter onto the top of her porridge. This was a treat, it made the porridge twice as delicious. But by the time she had steered the melting butter onto the right bits of the porridge, she had forgotten the question she wanted to ask.

Fru Ferndal moved slowly to her household tasks these days. Jenny had taken to trotting after her with a small, clean duster in her hand, ready to wipe any surfaces necessary. She loved Mama Ferndal and liked to feel she was helping her when she had that pain. When she had helped to make her own little bed, Fru Ferndal astonished her very much by telling her she must put on her Sunday clothes.

"Is it Sunday already, Mama? Then why isn't Papa ringing the church bell?"

Fru Ferndal bent down and hugged her suddenly. "No, it is not Sunday, sweetheart. But you are going on a journey. Fancy, all the way to Stockholm!"

"Then you must put on your Sunday clothes, too. Is Papa coming as well?"

Fru Ferndal shook her head and hurried down the little staircase again. "I haven't told her yet, Carl. Only that she is going to Stockholm. If she knew we—that she must go without us—she would begin to cry. And you know, that would make a very bad impression."

"Her clothes—have you packed them?"

"I'll do so later, when she's not noticing."

It seemed a strange morning altogether. Jenny noticed that Papa Ferndal hung about the house instead of working in the garden or cleaning the church. Mama Ferndal seemed busy upstairs, then she came down again and, seating herself by the wood fire where the dinner was cooking, pulled Jenny suddenly onto her knees and covered her with kisses.

When she set Jenny free again, Jenny looked at her earnestly and said, "Mama, are you a witch?"

"A witch, my daughter?"

"She's heard talk in the village already," Carl muttered.

Jenny bounced up and down on Fru Ferndal's knee. "Selma says witches work spells. What are spells? And they know what's going to happen. Do you know that?"

A curious look came into Fru Ferndal's face. "It is as good a way to tell her as any," she muttered to her husband. Then, to Jenny: "Bring me an egg, and a glass tumbler. Then we shall see what we shall see."

Jenny brought the egg very carefully, in case it got smashed. Fru Ferndal cracked it against the side of the tumbler, and let the white of the egg drop slowly into the glass. The yoke she emptied into the soup on the fire beside her, to make it richer.

"Now let us see——" The moonstone liquid moved sluggishly into shapes and circles. Fru Ferndal tilted the glass toward her a little.

"What do you see?" Jenny peered over her shoulder. Many a time, in winter, Mama Ferndal had shown her wonderful things in the fire. But this milky stuff was different. One would have to be a real witch to see anything in it at all.

Papa Ferndal stopped staring up at the painted clock, and half-turned, listening.

"I see a nice lady coming to take Jenny home with her on a visit. How wonderful for Jenny to see Stockholm! The carriage is coming nearer and nearer. . . . Jenny is going to ride in it like a Countess, think of that! It is only a hired carriage, not very grand, but someday Jenny shall have her own. She will travel through the whole world in it, like a queen. . . ."

"Will there be room in the carriage for you and Papa? Because I'm not going to Stockholm without you!" Jenny's mouth set in that firm line they both knew too well.

"Ah, Jenny, I'm not well enough to drive as far as Stockholm! But the lady will take you, she comes nearer and nearer. She——"

Suddenly somebody knocked on the door outside.

Somebody came sweeping into the room. A thin lady wearing a Stockholm bonnet and darned gloves. A lady with a face full of lines and temper. Not kind and gentle like Mama Ferndal's. The lady went straight to Jenny.

"What a plain-looking child! Come, Jenny, give your mama a kiss."

25

Jenny obediently turned her little face up toward Fru Ferndal who said gently, "The other way, love. There is your real mama."

But Jenny would not look the other way. She buried her face in Fru Ferndal's skirts instead. The two women went on talking over her head. "She is like my own child," Fru Ferndal was saying, "I could not possibly love her more. It broke my heart to ask you to take her away. But I know this illness, there is only one end to it. Better for Jenny to go now, where she can be taken care of properly."

"Yes, yes." The other's voice broke in, strained and cross, "but as for taking care of her properly, I have my profession—my teaching. And there is very little room in our flat in the Mäster Samuelsgränd. However, one must make the best of things I suppose. But I wish she were prettier. Good looks help one to make one's way in the world."

Fru Ferndal stroked the yellow mop of hair lying in her lap, then said, "One thing, I must ask you to remember. The child is a loving child. Love her, and you may rule her. Severity only rouses in her the spirit of combat. I would warn you not to do that."

The stranger looked startled; angry even. Was she being taught how to treat her own child? "Come, Jenny," she said sharply, "it is time for us to start on our way to Stockholm." Then, in gentler tones, "You will like to drive in a carriage, won't you?"

"Is it a big enough carriage to hold us all?"

"Quite big enough to hold you and me. Now, Jenny's

luggage, if you please. I will fetch the driver in to get it."

Fru Ferndal rose to show her where the little box stood, at the foot of the stairs. It was oval-shaped, made of thin birch bark with a leather handle. She could scarcely bear to think of the small dresses lying, neatly folded, inside. It was a relief when the driver stepped in and removed it, Fru Fellborg accompanying him out to the gate to show him where it must be put.

Fru Ferndal went back slowly into the room. Jenny was standing, very stiff and still, in the middle of it. Carl must have told her they were not going. He was drawing a very large handkerchief out of his pocket. He handed it to the child.

"This is for you to bawl and yell into," he told her casually, "because it is bigger than your own, so when you roar and cry as you drive away, it will mop up the tears faster."

Jenny's mouth had already opened; her eyes filled with tears. She winked the tears back and looked fiercely at him. "I'm not going to roar and cry. Why should I?"

"Oh, just because you're a baby yet. And Stockholm's a long way. If you cried all the way there, I'm sure I wouldn't be surprised."

"Then I won't cry a *drop*. I'm not a baby, I tell you!" Her mouth had closed in a mutinous line. He patted her on the shoulder, took her small hand in his, and led her out to the carriage. It was a poor, shabby-looking equipage, because Fru Fellborg couldn't afford any better. But the sight of it momentarily took away Jenny's

27

attention from leaving home. She climbed into it now quite happily, and waved as they drove away.

Carl Ferndal put his arm round his wife's shoulders as they walked back to the house. It was she who was crying. He wiped her eyes tenderly with the handkerchief Jenny had spurned. Seeing he was almost as broken hearted at losing the child as she was, she tried to joke, tremblingly, about it.

"That was a good idea, telling Jenny she would behave like a baby! You and I know, Carl, that 'tis easy to get her to go the opposite way."

"Aye. Tell her she can't do anything, and she'll do it right away! I was afraid she'd make a scene and upset you. And now, you're upset yourself, and so am I. But Fru Fellborg'll bring her back next summer, never fear! She's promised to come on a visit."

It was golden afternoon now. The white tower of the church seemed to pierce the blue sky. For miles around the fields lay shimmering in the heat. Fru Ferndal turned at the gate and looked at it all, as if she would never see it again. She knew that this summer would be her last.

Perhaps the shadow of her thought touched her husband's mind. At any rate, to distract her attention he asked quickly, "What was that nonsense you told her about riding in her own carriage one day like a queen?"

She looked up at him, startled. "Did I say that?"

"Yes, you did. It was all very well to say she was going to ride to Stockholm in a carriage, for so she was. But I'm the sacristan. A man employed about the church needs to stick to the truth—aye, and his wife too. What put all that fiddledeedee in your head?"

She said nothing, looking down at the ground again. She was remembering her mother, long ago in Finland, whom some people called a witch. And how she could read the future, and utter it too; but seldom remembered afterwards what she had said.

CHAPTER II

The woman who called herself Fru Fellborg sat in the carriage gazing out of the window. Her unwanted daughter gazed timidly up at her face to see if there was any love there. Then looked out of the window as well. They drove through a landscape still rural. Although nowadays Sollentuna is almost a suburb of Stockholm, it was far enough away in the year 1824. The length of the drive gave them both time for thought.

Jenny's mother had been born Anne-Marie Fellborg, the daughter of a Stockholm harbor-master and, after an unhappy marriage and a divorce, had taken her maiden name again. She had been brought up in a comfortable home and had had a good education. Now she had to work for a living. Her good education enabled her to run a small school in her Stockholm flat, with just enough time left to look after Amalia, her elder daughter.

Jenny was too much trouble. Fru Fellborg had to work hard all day and Amalia was old enough to fend for herself. So Jenny had been boarded out in the country, with the kind Ferndals who charged very little for her keep. The school had not been doing very well. Always there was a struggle to make ends meet; to feed and clothe Amalia properly and to find money enough for the rent. It was only an embarrassment to her and no pleasure, to be forced now to take Jenny back.

And the child sensed this perfectly well. Only once

did she speak during the long drive to the capital. Only once did she look up into the bitter face above her and ask, "Is Mama Ferndal my real mama or are you?"

"I am your real mama."

Jenny pursed her lips together and said not another word. For a child of four, this showed remarkable self-control. But now they were entering Stockholm at last. The child, distracted from keeping her tears back, gazed with awe at the tall gray and brown houses which shut out the sky; at the churches four times as big as the one at home; at the crowds in the streets as if it was Sunday.

"We are here," said her new mama.

The cab had stopped halfway along Mäster Samuels-gränd, a steep street lined with rather shabby houses. There were shops under them, and most of the shops were still open although it was evening now. The late summer and autumn had been very warm this year. People still sat before their doors, reading or sewing or merely gossiping. They looked up with interest at the cab, and some of them stared at Jenny.

"Make haste, child!" Fru Fellborg had paid the cabman, taken up Jenny's small piece of luggage in one hand, and was now pulling her toward a dark doorway with the other. They climbed up and up, till Jenny's little legs ached, and her mother's grip grew firmer. At last, here was the doorway, painted a shabby chocolate. Their steps had echoed up the stairway before them, for the door flew open. There stood a rather pale girl of about thirteen. She wore a big apron and held a wooden ladle in one hand. Drops of soup fell from the ladle on to the floor.

"Watch what you are about, Amalia!" Her mother told her sharply. Then, to the child tugging at her hand: "Jenny, this is your sister Amalia."

Amalia relinquished the ladle which her mother snatched from her, disappearing with it toward the kitchen. She knelt down and put her arms around Jenny. "You mustn't mind if she's cross," she whispered in Jenny's ear. "*I* don't mind. She's always cross."

Jenny hardly understood. She was dreadfully tired, and now the tears could no longer be stopped. The dark stairway behind her smelled of the street; the strange, big girl had soup spilled down her apron however kindly she spoke; and the house through the chocolate door looked like a trap.

Jenny was sobbing loudly as Amalia led her into it.

Her tears blinded her, so that she could scarcely see the room she was taken to. It was a big room and served as kitchen and schoolroom, too. A long table stretched from wall to wall at its farther end. The top was scored with names and blotted with ink. Two hard wooden benches ran down each side of the table, and piles of schoolbooks stood at one end of it, waiting for tomorrow's lessons.

Fru Fellborg turned from the soup she was stirring and said to Jenny, "Be quiet! Stop that noise!" Then to herself, as she went back to her cooking, "Oh heavens, what a day! What a headache I have!"

Jenny opened her very large mouth and bawled.

Suddenly the door of the bedroom opened. A little old lady came out. She was Fru Fellborg's mother, and trouble and poverty had turned her nature as sweet as they had turned the other's sour.

"Poor little one! Come to Granny, and she will give you some nice supper! A little of that hot soup, Anne-Marie, and a portion of bread. The child is worn out."

She sat down with the bowl in one hand, and took Jenny onto her knee. Her dress was clean and scented, not spotted with soup, and her hands were soft. She fed Jenny as if she were a baby again, spooning the soup into her mouth, and, when it was finished, dabbing Jenny's lips with her own handkerchief which smelled of lavender like her dress.

Jenny had stopped crying. Now she was half asleep. She scarcely felt the old lady taking off her clothes, putting on one of the frilly nightgowns from the birch-bark valise. But she felt herself lifted up, carried into the bedroom, and laid on a cot near the big bed Amalia and Fru Fellborg shared. Her arms still around the old lady's neck, she asked sleepily, "Are you another mama?"

"I am your grandmamma, and that is even better. Sleep well, my pet. Tomorrow night we will not be so tired, and then we can say our prayers."

Fru Fellborg's pupils were on holiday, which was why she had hurried to Sollentuna for Jenny while she was free. She would have been kind to the child if only she had not had to work so hard, and did not have a perpetual headache. Besides, it was an extra mouth to feed. Her payments to the Ferndals for Jenny's keep had been little enough. Here, in the city, food was twice as dear.

Amalia did her best. When their mother could spare her, she would take Jenny out into the parks and open

33

places of the city. The nearest to them was the Humlegården, a delightful place with grass and trees. It had a
wide path down the middle, where the smart towns-
people rode or drove.

Amalia loved the Humlegården, and couldn't understand why Jenny got bored with it so soon. Amalia liked
to see the elegant ladies drive past; to study the shape of
their bonnets, and to admire the handsome gentlemen
who sometimes rode alongside the carriages.

But to Jenny the grass was not real grass, since it was
bordered by houses; the trees were only town trees, not
the slender birches about the lake near Sollentuna, and
she hated the noise of the traffic which hurt her ears.
And worst of all there weren't any flowers to pick.

"I want to go back to the country!" She would say to
her grandmother. "Why can't I go home to my other
mama?"

"Because she is ill, Jenny. This is your home now.
Come, dry your tears and let me tell you a story."

The old lady's stories were mostly from the Bible
which she almost knew by heart. She told them and
Jenny listened, storing them up in her mind. The story
of the Ass that talked. Of the Woman who lost a pearl.
Of the Miracles of Our Lord. . . .

It was this early teaching that so impressed Jenny, and
which she never forgot. She would fix her large,
thoughtful eyes—the only part of her that was pretty—
upon the old lady, drinking in every word. When she
was with her grandmother, she was happy because she
knew she was loved. But all the same, she forgot how to
laugh, or run, or play. If she did any of these things

inside the flat, her mother might easily scold her.

There was one room she was not allowed to go into. That was Fru Fellborg's parlor. This was the last evidence of former gentility to which the harbor master's daughter still clung. All the work of the house might clutter up the kitchen, and there was only one bedroom for them to sleep in. But still, Fru Fellborg had her parlor, like any lady of quality.

It had a wallpaper of pale striped satin and chairs covered with stuff embroidered with roses. There was a white porcelain stove in one corner, but the stove was never lit because fuel was too expensive. In summer, the room was pleasant to sit in. Neighbors who called, were led into it proudly. In winter, it was cold as the North Pole. Then Fru Fellborg would explain that unfortunately the parlor was having something done to it, and she took her guests into the kitchen instead.

Amalia thought the grandest thing in the room was the gilt clock on the little table by the window. Jenny liked the piano best. It had been bought, at great sacrifice, for Fru Fellborg to give piano lessons. Some of the older pupils were allowed to practice on it, too. In winter, a little portable stove was carried in and placed near the piano. But most of them developed chilblains all the same.

Jenny was not allowed to touch the piano. She wasn't supposed to enter the room at all, though she might accompany Amalia when Amalia went in, once a week, to dust it. The piano was generally closed, with a strip of felt over its keys. If Fru Fellborg was out shopping, Amalia would sometimes open the piano, remove the

35

strip, and allow Jenny to pick out one or two notes. But both girls were frightened for fear their mother might come back and hear them. Jenny kept listening all the time she made these delightful noises. And Amalia shut the lid again in a very few minutes.

One day Amalia was dusting and Jenny had already scrambled onto the music stool, for Mama was out shopping and the chance too good to be missed. Suddenly Amalia craned her head and shoulders out of the window, staring down into the street.

A burst of bugle music came into the room. Jenny slipped off the stool again and ran to Amalia. She ducked her head under her sister's arm and peered over the window ledge. The music came nearer. Now it sounded shrill and loud, just below them. A regiment of Swedish cavalry swung down the street, and the buglers were blowing a fanfare. It was a long fanfare, quite an elaborate one.

Jenny listened to it, her head on one side. Then she ducked away from Amalia again, ran back to the piano and began picking out the tune on the keys. Softly the door opened while she was playing. Her grandmother stood there, listening. Jenny began, happily, to play the fanfare over again. But she was interrupted this time. Fru Fellborg entered the flat, having heard the tune all the way upstairs. She was furious.

"Come off that stool at once! How dare you soil the ivory keys with your sticky fingers!"

All Jenny's happiness vanished. She had been singing the tune, too, but now the notes trembled and died away. She slammed down the lid of the piano and ran out of the room. The old lady turned to her daughter.

"Why so sharp with the child, Anne-Marie? You should admire her talent, not punish her for having it. She copied that fanfare exactly. I really thought it was Amalia practicing. And she has such a sweet little voice."

Fru Fellborg passed her hand over her face wearily. "Potatoes have gone up in price again. Really one hardly knows what to feed the girls on. . . . And Jenny's singing gets on my nerves. All this craze for music must come from her father. Niclas is just as bad. . . ."

One evening Niclas Lind turned up. He had been having one of his usual spells in the Debtor's Prison when Jenny first came to Stockholm. This evening she had been out with Amalia, and the autumn dusk had come down before they were aware. Jenny had been entranced by the swinging lamps in the streets and the smell of winter, still far away but approaching steadily.

A rich, full voice reached them from the parlor as they re-entered the flat. A man's voice, singing a jolly drinking song to the plucked sounds of an accompaniment. Not caring what punishment might come, Jenny ran into the parlor where she was forbidden. It was warm and cozy for once. Miraculously, someone had lit the big porcelain stove. Someone had set out a meal on the marble table. There were sandwiches half demolished, a bottle of schnapps, and a glass half full.

The song twanged abruptly to an end. The man sitting astride the piano stool put down his guitar and held out his arms to Jenny.

"So this is my little daughter? We don't remember

each other, do we? You were small enough when we first met!"

After a moment's consideration Jenny walked forward and let him kiss her. No, she didn't remember him. Other little girls had fathers, so she supposed she could have one, too. Mama was sitting on a chair by the stove, looking quite different. She had her best dress on for one thing, and her hair shiny and curled, and she did not frown once at Jenny for coming into the forbidden room.

The big man was strumming on his guitar again. "They tell me Jenny can sing. Come along. Join in with Papa!"

At first Jenny only hummed softly, with sidelong glances toward Mama, who always told her to stop because a loud noise hurt her head. Then she sang louder and louder. Presently Niclas Lind stopped and made her repeat the words of the song. "They are by our great national poet, Bellman, and must not be forgotten or slurred over. Sing the song correctly, sweetheart, or not at all!"

It was a happy evening for Jenny. Here was somebody else who loved music, too! She felt a pang of disappointment when her father went away. Why couldn't he and Mama live together like other peoples' parents? Yet, young as she was, she sensed the different attitude toward life which seemed to make it impossible. Her mother driven by duty and taking no pleasure in life; her father who thought life was made for enjoyment and nothing else.

So Niclas Lind disappeared again, leaving only his

38

songs behind. Jenny tried hard to remember them. She repeated the words to herself, as well as the tunes. Some of the words were not at all suitable for a child of her age; some were sad and about death, but Jenny liked the sad ones best somehow; their tunes were usually the prettiest.

And every few months, before she had quite forgotten the last ones he had taught her, Niclas Lind would turn up again. Again the big stove would be lit in his honor, and the best food and drink set before him. Anne-Maria Fellborg couldn't help herself. However much she hardened her heart against him after he had gone, she still melted before his presence like ice in the sun.

But now, she suspected he came to see Jenny. To hear that amazingly crystal-clear voice, and to try it out on new songs for his amusement. He came for that, and to borrow money from Jenny's mother as well. Sometimes she lent some to him, when she had any to spare.

CHAPTER III

Winter came, with long, dark days and frozen sludge along the Mäster Samuelsgränd. No grand carriages drove through the Humlegården now; they were laid up in favor of sledges. The old city stood on the edge of Lake Malar, and sometimes the ice was so thick, people could drive all the way along its coast, with the sledge bells ringing and the lights of Stockholm behind them.

Spring returned. The snow melted and ran away into the gutters. One day Niclas Lind, having unaccustomed money in his pocket, took Jenny and Amalia for a drive in a hired gig, to Djurgården. This was a wonderful park —where the young beech trees were putting out leaves already, and the ground below them was white with wind flowers.

When Jenny saw them, she began to cry. "I want to go back to the country!" she sobbed. "To dear Mama Ferndal and Sollentuna!"

Lind dried her tears and promised that when summer came he would drive her there. But by the time it was summer he had forgotten his promise, and in any case, Fru Ferndal was dead. Her pain had finished her at last. He took Jenny instead, to the great harbor called Skeppsholmen and together they leaned over the barrier and pointed out the ships to each other. Swedish ships with the well-known blue and yellow flag; Danish ships from across the Sound, flaunting their famous Dannebrog;

four-masted barques from Russia and Finland loaded with grain. There were fishermen, too, fishing from square wooden rafts. When they saw anyone landing a fish, Niclas would clap his hands and call "Brava!" loudly, even though they were too far off for the fishermen to hear.

So the memory of Sollentuna sank away into the back of Jenny's mind and was almost forgotten.

She had started lessons now at her mother's school. She was much the youngest of the pupils and found it very hard to keep up with them. Fru Fellborg made no allowance for that. She scolded Jenny harshly when she made mistakes, or drummed on the top of her head with her thimble. Jenny would have made more mistakes still, had not Amalia helped her. As it was, she got into trouble every day, though Amalia and one of the older girls called Louise Johanson shielded her when they could.

Her grandmother wasn't there to protect her any more. The old lady had only been waiting for admission to the Stockholm Widows' Home. Now she had gone to live there, and Jenny's only happy hours were those she spent on visits to her. Fortunately her mother was only too glad to get rid of her, so she could go very often.

Today there is a famous skyscraper store on the site of the old Home. But the Home was an elegant building, a little palace built in the eighteenth century and abandoned to charity about a hundred years later. It was built around three sides of a square. Tall railings and an imposing gateway separated it from the street. An outside double staircase curved up to the front door, which was on the first floor of the building. Another door under this staircase led to the apartments of the steward and his wife. If either of them was about, they would smile and nod to Jenny when she arrived and climbed up the steps to visit her grandmother.

Some of the widows had their own apartments, too. They were the comparatively rich ones. The others, like Jenny's grandmother, had each her own corner of a vast hall or salon. It had once seen grand balls and had come down in the world since then. Still, the big room was attractive because it was so clean and orderly. All around its walls were little beds in recesses. Each had its curtains of blue-and-white checked material which were drawn across to hide the beds in the daytime. This gave the room the appearance of being lined in blue-and-white cotton.

Beside each bed-recess stood a chest of drawers and one chair. In the middle of the room there were tables for ironing, for goffering caps, for mixing dough, and for all the little duties and pleasures in which the old ladies indulged. Yet the room still seemed quite big enough, it was so vast.

Jenny loved her visits here, and the old ladies loved having her. It was somebody young about the place. Because they smiled at her and spoke kindly, she became, for an hour or two anyway, the bouncing, singing little girl she had been in Sollentuna. She loved jokes and laughter. Sometimes she tore from one end of the great hall to the other, swerving to avoid the tables and the old ladies, and shrieking with joy when one of them caught her as she ran by.

But when it came time to go home, her spirits would die away and she would become once more the dull, heavy child that her mother always saw. Amalia would arrive to take her back through the crowded streets. And she would climb the dark stairway and enter through the chocolate door with a feeling of hopeless misery.

So time went on. Now she was nine years old. Her grandmother still welcomed and looked forward to her visits, but she was old and frail and couldn't stand too much teasing and jumping around her. That summer— the summer of 1830—there was a heat wave. The city lay sweltering under a blazing sun which scarcely seemed to go down at all. In the afternoons, all the old ladies used to retire behind their blue-and-white curtains for a siesta. Jenny was told to be quiet, though she could sing if she liked. Singing often soothed one to sleep.

The windows were thrown open wide to let in as much air as possible. Jenny sat on a window sill and sang to the cat belonging to the establishment. He was a large gray cat called Vasa. He had a blue ribbon round his neck. It had been an old hair ribbon of Jenny's, and his fur was so deep, the blue was almost hidden by it. His eyes opened and closed again into slits, as he listened to Jenny's singing. Her voice floated through the window, away from the room where all but one of the old ladies snored behind their checked curtains.

The remaining old lady still sat on her rocking chair. She was expecting a visitor. She had not been at the Home very long, but already everyone had heard about "My niece, who is personal maid to the famous dancer, Mademoiselle Lundberg." Some of the old ladies thought she boasted too much. They sniffed, and said that the stage was not respectable. They said, who was Mademoiselle Lundberg anyway?

But the old lady paid no attention. She lived on the weekly visits from her niece. Then she could hear all about the latest productions at the Royal Opera House, and the famous people who praised Mademoiselle Lundberg's performances. And (because she was so old, and sometimes so confused) she had almost got to thinking that her niece and the dancer were one and the same.

So now, on this hot afternoon, she sat and rocked gently back and forth. Beside her on the table, was a pot of coffee, and a plate of freshly made coffeecake. Jenny's little song accompanied the rocking:

> *"I had a silver thimble,*
> *To show me how to sew,*
> *But ah! the thread got broken—*
> *So now I scarcely know!"*

Vasa's claws moved lazily in and out with delight. The old lady rocked in time to the song. "Go on singing, Jenny! Sing that old song about the moon. You know the one that I like." It was a melancholy, tender song that Niclas Lind sometimes sang. Jenny switched over to it at once. Instead of the jolly rhythm of the other, the long, pure notes sang out through the window, arresting the steps of a young woman who had just crossed the courtyard from the street and was about to climb the stairway up to the door of the Home.

44

Jenny didn't notice her. When the song came to an end, she began to untie Vasa's ribbon and tie it again more elegantly. She was so busy at this, she scarcely noticed Mademoiselle Lundberg's maid enter the room. The maid was finely dressed in some of her mistress's cast-off clothes. She gave quite a fashionable air to the room, as she went over to her aunt, bent down and kissed her.

"Who is that little girl?" she asked. "The girl with the wonderful voice?"

The old lady couldn't remember. "Her grandmother lives here, so she comes to visit. Ask her yourself."

Jenny heard a rustle of silk as the young lady bent over her. "What is your name, my dear?"

The child looked up. "Johanna-Maria-Lind-but-they-call-me-Jenny."

"And where do you live?"

"Number Forty, Mäster Samuelsgränd."

The young lady nodded and patted her cheek. She went back to the table where her old aunt had already begun to pour out coffee. Jenny was vaguely conscious that they were talking about her, but she didn't bother to listen. Vasa was finding his new collar uncomfortable. She had to unknot and then knot it again.

Then the bell of St. Jakob's Church rang out the hour for her to go home. All the old ladies were emerging from behind their curtains because it was coffee time for them, too. Jenny's grandmother kissed her good-by affectionately. She dropped a curtsey toward the grand young lady in the bonnet scalloped with lace, then ran down the stone stairway outside, and so home.

It was a few days after this that a carriage drove through Mäster Samuelsgränd. The shabby street was quite unaccustomed to such a sight, which provoked much attention. The evening was warm, and most people were sitting at their windows after the day's work. They hung out to see where it was bound for. It stopped at Number Forty.

Jenny was having her supper when the knock came at the door. Fru Fellborg was ironing at the other end of the table and Amalia, who had finished supper, sat mending by the open window. She had not dared to look out of it at the sound of the carriage below. But she paused, listening, as footsteps echoed, climbing the bare stairway. Up farther and farther they came. They stopped just outside the chocolate door. Then came a knock, gentle but firm.

"Amalia, open the door!" ordered her mother.

Amalia laid her darning needle on the sill and opened the door. She gasped at the sight of the stranger who stood there. A lady, a lovely lady, dressed exactly like the ones who drove in the Humlegården! The lady stepped forward into the room. She held the full silken folds of her dress in one hand. In the other was a tiny parasol, ostrich-feather-tipped, with an ivory handle.

Jenny laid down her spoon and stared.

Fru Fellborg stared, too. She stared at the lovely face under the white silk bonnet, and saw at once that it was covered with rice powder, and that the curved lips were touched with coral. She stiffened. This was an actress. She was sure of it!

The lady took another step forward, her lace cloak

46

breathing out perfume, the tiny feathers around her bonnet moving in spite of the still air.

"My name is Mademoiselle Lundberg," she said in a very sweet voice, "and I have come to see a little girl called Jenny Lind."

The Lundberg! Fru Fellborg knew all about her. She was a famous dancer at the Royal Opera House, where they performed ballets in most of the operas because dancing was a passion with the Swedes and the Danish people, too. The newspapers talked of The Lundberg as if she were something unique. They filled their pages with trash about her. What had such a woman to do with Number Forty, Mäster Samuelsgränd?

And what could she possibly want with Jenny?

The woman had actually advanced around the end of the table and was looking down at Jenny now. "About nine years old . . ." she murmured as if speaking to herself. Then—"So you are Jenny, my dear? The little girl with the wonderful voice!"

"How do you know about it?" asked Jenny's mother sharply.

The Lundberg turned to her with a gracious movement. "Forgive me. I must explain. My maid heard Jenny singing when she visited her aunt at the Widows' Home. She has raved about her ever since. She so excited my curiosity——"

"Ah!" Fru Fellborg's lips set in a tight line. "So it is curiosity which brings you to our poor home?"

"Not entirely. If your Jenny's voice merits training, I am willing to help her. But I must hear her first. May I?"

For a moment Amalia thought her mother was going to refuse. The sweet if willful manner in which the request was made had made Fru Fellborg angrier still. She stood there, rigid, with the iron in her hand. The dancer smiled at her, repeating "May I?"

Fru Fellborg laid the iron down and turned to the child. "Sing then," she ordered curtly, "sing something to satisfy our visitor. Then perhaps she will go."

But Jenny was frightened now. She sat there, her mouth firmly shut.

"Oh, one must not ask a favor like that!" The lovely lady bent down and put an arm round the child's taut little body. "Come, to please me! Sing just the little song you were singing to your cat!"

The arm gave Jenny confidence. She began to hum the simple air. Her voice sounded faltering and husky at first. She didn't want to sing that song anyway, it was only for Vasa. She began instead, to sing another. And presently she forgot her angry mother and sang out loudly and clearly.

"Amazing!" The Lundberg listened, entranced. "Why, that's one of Bellman's songs! Who taught the child that?"

"Her father." Fru Fellborg said dryly. "He thinks himself a musician, too."

The lady was fumbling in the elegant silk bag which swung from her wrist. She pulled a letter from it and laid it on the table. "This is an introduction to the Singing Master at the Royal Opera House. I brought it along in case———. But now that I have heard Jenny sing, I *know* that he can turn her into one of the greatest and most remarkable ornaments of our stage!"

"The stage? Our Jenny go on the stage?" Fru Fellborg was horrified. "No!" she cried passionately. "We are a respectable family!"

The Lundberg looked at her with astonishment. "But you don't understand! The children trained at the Opera are most carefully looked after. Jenny would get all her schooling free, yes, and her clothes and food. It would be wicked, wicked, not to do something with such a wonderful gift from God! Herr Craelius has only to hear her to undertake her training. This is a letter to him——"

Clothes, food, and training free! And she had called Jenny's voice a gift from God. Maybe she wasn't so bad. . . . But then, the surroundings, the atmosphere of the Opera! Fru Fellborg had hated and suspected the theater and theatrical people all her life. Even Jenny's grandmother had hated it, too.

The brief struggle seemed to be over. Fru Fellborg picked up the letter and held it out.

"I thank you, Mademoiselle, for your interest in my child," she said coldly, "but I decline your proposal."

The dancer took the letter from her, weighed it in her gloved hand, then laid it back on the table. Her own voice was cold and not nearly so pretty when she spoke again.

"You are shutting the door on your own child's future. This is the key to it. I shall leave the letter behind, in case you think better of it."

The door closed again. She was gone. But still her perfume lingered on the air, and the rustle of her silk skirts came to them faintly as she descended the stairs once more. Then they heard the carriage move off. The sound of the horses' hoofs fading along the street.

Jenny finished her supper, washed up her little bowl and spoon and, at a glance from Fru Fellborg, went into the bedroom to undress. Her mother followed her to draw the curtains and shut out some of the evening sunlight. Only Amalia was left alone in the room.

Fru Fellborg came back again and began to tidy things up for the night. She put away the ironing cloth and tidied the rest of the table. There lay the crumpled newspaper, which she needed to light the stove next morning. But where was the letter? She was too tired to worry about that tonight. . . .

Amalia and Jenny shared the big bed now, and their mother slept in the single one by the wall. Jenny was still dazed by their sudden visitor. As she lay by Amalia's side, she went over all that the strange lady had said.

"Amalia!" she whispered. "Did the lady mean that someday I could be a real singer, and look like her?"

"Yes, Jenny. It was a shame that Mother doesn't want you to."

"I could never look like her. Never. But I do want to learn how to sing."

"It's a shame!" Amalia said again, hugging her little sister tighter to her. She could feel Jenny trembling with disappointment. "Never mind!" she put her lips close to Jenny's ear and whispered back. "Maybe something will happen to change her mind."

"But the letter! She'll tear it up——"

"No she won't. I've hidden it someplace safe!"

CHAPTER IV

Autumn had come now. The leaves were falling from the trees in the Humlegården. People no longer kept their windows open along Mäster Samuelsgränd, because the evening air had turned chilly. Soon the lights would go up in the Royal Opera House, and Lake Malar begin to be frozen over. Soon, too, Fru Fellborg's pupils would start their lessons again after the summer holidays.

Only two or three of them had promised to come back. Fru Fellborg was worried. She was a good teacher and knew it. But she did not realize how her scolding tongue frightened the children, so that several of them had begged to be taken away and sent to another school. Jenny's special friend, Louise Johanson, was one of those. Louise was now old enough to earn her living. She was to be apprenticed to a dressmaker. Louise was poor, and had paid very little for her board and education, so Fru Fellborg didn't mind about losing her. But Jenny wept.

It was a different matter about Greta, who was Fru Fellborg's richest and best-paying pupil. Her parents were abroad. She had even been given the little parlor all to herself, because her father was so well-off and she had always been accustomed to the best. But now her parents had come back to Sweden, and Greta was able to tell them how unhappy she was.

They wrote to Fru Fellborg. "Greta's not coming back," she told Amalia, letting the letter fall into her lap. "With food so expensive, and the price of wood for the stove getting worse and worse, I'm sure I don't know how we shall get through the winter."

Jenny had crept into the room and stood listening. During the weeks since the dancer's visit, she had thought of nothing but the lost opportunity of getting away from a home she hated as much as Greta did. She had forgotten to laugh. She was always afraid of doing the wrong things. She even forgot to sing.

"Mother," Amalia said, "would it have made things easier if the Opera School had paid for—for one of us after all?"

Fru Fellborg dried her eyes and straightened her back. "It's silly to cry over spilled milk. I did what I thought right. Perhaps if I had known——"

"Mother," Amalia said again, "it isn't too late yet, to present that letter of introduction to Herr Craelius. Is it?"

"But the letter was lost."

"Have—have you looked everywhere? Below the big cupboard, for example?"

"How could it possibly have got there! I tell you, I left it on the edge of the ironing table."

"A draught from the door might have blown it under the cupboard. At least let us look!"

Amalia went down on her hands and knees and felt beneath it. Presently she brought out the letter.

"Fancy!" her mother said, wondering. "Who would have thought the draught could have blown it so far!"

This happened just before dinnertime. The two girls eyed their mother as she dished out the meal wrapped in thought. Jenny knew better than to ask her decision. But she could eat nothing for the sick excitement that welled in her throat. After the dishes were washed, Fru Fellborg said brusquely: "I am going to the Home to consult your grandmama and see what she thinks. Stay indoors, Jenny, until I come back."

That made it harder than ever. The afternoon dragged along slowly. Time stood still, so that the sunshine seemed scarcely to move on the wall. But it had almost faded when they heard the door open, and Fru Fellborg enter the flat.

"Mama! Oh, Mama!" Jenny could scarcely speak. She looked imploringly at her mother's face.

"Well! Your grandmama was very upset, as I knew she would be. Does she not know the dangers of theater life as well as I do? But nevertheless, it is not she who must find the money for you this winter."

Jenny stood still, silent. Amalia took hope. "It's not very late. There's still time——"

"Go and get your best dress on." Fru Fellborg ordered Jenny. "And put on a thick coat. The evenings are chilly now."

Amalia cast a triumphant glance at her little sister, then hustled her into the bedroom and began to help her to dress feverishly. At last Amalia stuck her cold little hands into the muff that Greta had given her. It was her chief pride and glory.

"There! You may borrow it if you like. When you're cold you can't sing properly. For mercy's sake keep the shabby patch against your chest. Let the best bit of fur show. Greta gave it to me because she was ashamed of it. But it looks well enough if only you hold it properly."

Fru Fellborg held the precious letter in her hand when they stepped out into the street.

Dusk was falling already. "Bang, bang" went the shutters across the windows of Mäster Samuelsgränd, as people began to light their lamps and shut out the nip in the air. Fru Fellborg walked very quickly, as if afraid she might change her mind. Jenny stumbled and ran after her.

They left the poorer quarter of the town and entered the wide, fashionable streets running down to the water. The sky was green above it, and the lamplighters were already crossing the bridges, striking their long poles upward lighting one lamp after another. Usually Jenny liked to stand still and watch them. Now she had no eyes for anything except the white letter glimmering in her mother's hand.

Now they approached the opera house. It was said, at that time, to have the best acoustics in Europe. Heavy stone carvings frowned down upon a vast flight of steps leading up to the triple doors. Fru Fellborg faltered at last, as she climbed them. She looked wildly about her, then suddenly bent down and clutched Jenny to her breast.

"My lamb! I can't take you farther to this wicked place! Let us go home——"

It was almost the first sign of tenderness she had ever shown to the child. At another time Jenny would have melted; would have flung her arms around her mother's neck. Now she merely clutched Amalia's beautiful muff closer to her and stood obstinately still.

"I won't go home," she said.

"Jenny! Obey me at once!"

But Jenny had noticed the note of hysteria in her mother's voice. When that happened, one only had to be firm. "Besides," she added cleverly, "my boots hurt. The soles are too thin. You said I needed a new pair. Perhaps this Herr Crae—Craelius will pay for them."

Her mother gave a long sigh and began the upward climb once more. Jenny climbed after her, triumphant. Now they were facing a splendid gentleman wearing the royal livery because the opera house belonged to the King. Fru Fellborg held out the letter and faltered a few words. The gentleman said, "You should have come by the side door, Madame. Follow me if you please."

He led them through a vast, gilded foyer into a narrow passage behind. Here they were faced by an iron stairway leading to offices above the stage. Fru Fellborg would not have dared, now, to tell the crimson-clad gentleman she had changed her mind. She followed him meekly, up two flights of the staircase and along a passage with green baize doors lining one side of it.

One of the doors swung open as they passed by. The gentleman paused to say grandly, "You may obtain a view of the stage through that door. Take a step forward, little girl. Don't be afraid!"

"Herr Craelius——" muttered Fru Fellborg, not wishing to wait an instant. But the attendant who had come through the door was holding it open, so Jenny ran forward and peeped through.

At first, it was so dark, she saw nothing at all. She seemed to be looking down into a deep black hole pierced by flickering lights. They were the candles attached to the desks of the orchestra, and the orchestra had paused in its rehearsal. Suddenly the conductor's baton rapped its signal, and music swelled out of the blackness, filling the air with sound.

"A lovely tune! A lovely tune!" Jenny laughed and clapped her hands. But nobody heard her, she was so far away from the performers. Her mother pulled her back through the door again. It swung shut and the music was cut off as with a knife.

But the tune still went on in her head, taking away all her fears. She followed the grand gentleman quite happily now. This place, where they even made music out of the dark, was where she wanted to be.

Another door was opened. They were in a small office. An elderly man looked up from a seat at a desk. He had small, twinkling eyes and a large white beard and his coat was covered with snuff. Fru Fellborg curtseyed, then advanced with unusual timidity.

"Herr Craelius?"

"At your service, Madame."

She held out the letter toward him. He glanced with some astonishment at the shabby, weather-beaten woman before him, and the ugly child clutching a muff. Then he read the letter; glanced at the child again.

"So your name is Jenny Lind, little one? And you want to become a Child of the Opera someday, eh?"

"Not someday, sir. Now." The large, obstinate mouth had set until for one second she looked like her mother.

Herr Craelius sighed. He was a kindly man, always besieged by mothers who thought their children's voices phenomenal. He knew, too, that The Lundberg was given to sudden enthusiasms. He did not believe what she had written. He picked up a box of sweetmeats and held them out toward Jenny.

"Fill your mouth with one of these, child. Then come back in a year or two if you must. You are too young."

Jenny's eyes filled with tears. She disregarded the box. "Please, may I not sing?"

He shrugged his shoulders; put back the box on the edge of the desk. "Sing then. But I warn you——"

He was interrupted by Jenny's soft, clear voice. She sang with her hands in her muff. She sang the tune she had just heard the orchestra playing. It was in her mind already and she wanted to sing it. It was full of intricate phrases, but she remembered them all without fault, until suddenly she stopped in the middle of one of them.

Herr Craelius listened, amazed. Never, never had he heard a voice of such purity. And the child had even grown beautiful as she sang! The face was no longer heavy; it had transformed itself into an expression of joy and delight.

"Continue!" He begged. "Go on! Go on!"

"Then the door shut," explained Jenny, once more plain and dull.

Fru Fellborg said quickly, "She listened through one of the doors in the passage. It is the air the orchestra was playing."

"And she had never heard it before?" But he looked

at Jenny, who shook her head.

"No, sir. But I like it. I would like to learn the end."

Herr Craelius sprang up from his seat so suddenly, they were quite startled. He embraced Jenny. "So you shall, my treasure. So you shall!" Then he hesitated, struck by an uncomfortable thought. "But you are under the age for us here! This letter says you are only nine. I must ask permission of the Count to teach you."

Jenny and her mother glanced at each other. Who was the Count? He sounded frightening somehow. Herr Craelius said to the uniformed gentleman who still stood by, "Go and ask His Excellency to step in here for a moment. Tell him I wish him to hear the voice of a new candidate for the Opera School."

It seemed, as they waited, that Herr Craelius had become nervous himself. He clasped and unclasped his large hands, frowning. Then the door opened again. The Count was a majestic old man who brought in such an air of power and authority that Craelius, who was First Singing Teacher, seemed suddenly to shrink and become insignificant. The newcomer was a Court Official of the highest rank, and the affairs of the Royal Opera had been placed in his hands by the King.

Jenny and her mother both curtseyed instinctively. He ignored them. He had taken in Jenny's age and looks at a glance. "What is this nonsense, Craelius? Is this the child? You know as well as I do, we cannot accept anyone so young."

"But, Your Excellency, her voice! And I have here a

special recommendation from Mademoiselle Lundberg——"

"The Lundberg!" The tall old man shrugged his shoulders disdainfully. "You should know better than to take her recommendations seriously! All her geese are swans."

Herr Craelius spoke more earnestly still. "Excellency, if I may venture to say so, you are making a grave mistake. This child's voice, properly trained, will bring glory to our Opera. Never once, in all my lifetime of teaching, have I heard such a voice. I beg of you, hear her at least. Then if you still refuse to accept her——"

"Dear me, you are becoming quite heated, my dear fellow! And if I refuse, what happens next?"

"I propose to teach her myself, without any fees."

"You know the regulations regarding age. The Royal Opera House is not a crèche for infants."

"No, Excellency. But you have the power to set the regulations aside. Let her sing!"

The Count looked down from his great height at Jenny. "Sing, child!" He commanded.

But the voice was sharp and cold. And Jenny had now forgotten, in her fright, the tune the orchestra played. She stood, white-faced and silent, until her mother, in desperation, pulled at her skirts.

"Sing Jenny? Sing anything, sing one of the songs your Papa taught you——"

At the thought of her gay, laughing papa, Jenny suddenly relaxed. But it was one of his few sad tunes which came into her head; the famous Bacchic Ode by the loved Swedish poet, Bellman:

> *"Drink out thy glass,*
> *See Death upon thee waiteth,*
> *Sharpens his sword,*
> *And on thy threshold stands!*

The clear, pure notes uttered by a child held a terrible poignancy. Her voice seemed to search the very heart. She sang the song to the end, and when she had finished, both the old men had tears in their eyes. It had been an unearthly experience, like going into a wood by moonlight and hearing a nightingale sing.

For a few seconds, after the last note had ended, nobody spoke. Jenny stood waiting, her hands in her muff.

Then the Count took out a fine silk handkerchief and blew his nose. "You are right, Craelius. This is a clear case for making an exception to our usual rules."

He turned abruptly to Fru Fellborg. "You are her mother? Be pleased to return here tomorrow. We accept your daughter as a pupil of the Royal Opera School. We shall make ourselves responsible for her keep and her lessons. The contract will be ready for you to sign tomorrow."

CHAPTER V

The children of the Opera School were boarded out in suitable homes, though they came to the opera house for some of their lessons. It was arranged that Jenny should remain with her mother and be taught the usual subjects from her. The contract said: "Piano, Religion, French, History, Geography, Writing, Arithmetic and Drawing." Fru Fellborg was to be paid for giving those lessons. She was also given an allowance for "food, fire, furniture and clothing," and she had to promise to give her daughter "a Mother's care."

Fru Fellborg signed the contract gladly. Was she not doing all that, anyway, without any payment till now?

But there were other lessons, which only the opera house could give. Herr Craelius taught Jenny singing as he had promised. She had also to learn to walk and hold herself gracefully. She was taught elocution as well, and as she had a beautiful speaking voice, this was easy. She was taught Plastique Poses and how to make gestures while she was singing. She grew less lumpy and awkward. But nobody could ever call her a pretty child. It was only when she sang that she became, somehow, beautiful.

Those lessons were held in the opera house itself. It was a delight to Jenny to get away from dreary Mäster Samuelsgränd and scamper up the back stairway of the great building, to the big room where they held their practice. An elderly Frenchwoman, Mademoiselle Bayard, presided over them there. She wore tight bodices buttoned down the front, and a frizzed fringe of hair peeping out from under her cap. She had not been back to France for many years, but she still spoke of it as her beloved country.

"Queen Désirée, too, is a Frenchwoman," she would say with satisfaction, adding, "She and I both have the same French hearts beating beneath our bodices."

The pupils would giggle at that. And at her always calling the Queen "Désirée" instead of the Swedish form, Desideria, like everyone else in Sweden. For the rest, she tried to teach them to speak French with the proper accent. The only criticism she ever allowed herself to make of the Queen was that, having been born Désirée Cléry, the daughter of a Marseilles silk merchant, she had, of course, the atrocious Marseillaise accent.

"Guard yourselves, *mes chéres élèves,* from such an accent!" she would say, adding, "I, of course, am a Parisian. There, they speak the best French in the world."

Occasionally, as Jenny grew older, she would be allowed, with the other pupils, to be present at an opera performance. The Queen always, the King sometimes, would be in the Royal Box if a new opera was being given. Jenny would fix her large eyes on Desideria and think how strange it was that the daughter of a silk merchant should become Queen of Sweden! But hardly more strange than that she, Jenny, should be a Child of the Royal Opera School.

When the long, dark winters settled over Stockholm, the lights of the opera house blazed out all the more clearly. The water under the bridges turned to green ice, and Jenny would hurry home, after her singing lessons, over the cobbled streets from which mounds of snow had been swept into the gutters. Sometimes the sky would be lit by the flickering flames of the Northern Dancers, which was what people called the Northern Lights. But she never saw the real dancer, Mademoiselle Lundberg, again. It never happened that she received a ticket for any performance in which The Lundberg was dancing. And how could that beautiful creature remember the little girl who had caught her momentary attention?

The spring would come. Then last performances would be held, and when the ice broke up and the wild geese flew back over the city, the opera house would fall silent and empty. The sun lingered longer; rose higher. And the Opera School closed for the season.

Queen Desideria and her hook-nosed King would leave Stockholm for their palace in the country. Everybody left Stockholm who could. And Jenny left Stockholm, too. The pupils were given a free holiday, to refresh them after their hard work during the winter. They were sent, under the care of Mademoiselle Bayard, to a little island in the Baltic Sea.

Now Jenny saw the country once more; the real Swedish country she had never visited since the long-ago days in Sollentuna. They crossed over in a boat, she and the other girls of the Opera School, Charlotte, Mathilda, and Fanny. The waters of the Baltic were restless and white-capped. The boat rocked, and Mademoiselle Bayard sat very quiet with a handkerchief pressed to her mouth.

Somewhere inside the boat was the piano which they were obliged to take with them. They were only staying in a peasant's wooden house, where such luxuries were unknown.

Jenny, who was much the youngest, was always first off the boat. The wooden landing stage stretched into the water waiting to receive them. Each girl carried a valise of birch bark, just like the one Jenny's clothes were packed in long ago. (Birch bark is cheaper than leather and easier to obtain in a place like Sweden.) Then two sailors would heave the little square piano onto a trolley and run it up to the house.

The house stood on a plateau of rock, its painted windows looking straight over the water. The old peasant woman who owned it, and let it in summer, did the cooking in a small shed in which she also slept, and brought the food across to the one living room that filled the ground floor of the house.

After watching the piano being carefully put in position, Mademoiselle Bayard would climb the little staircase and take possession of the best bedroom, the one facing the bay. Jenny shared it with her. The other three girls shared the room opposite, which looked over the sparse fields of the island, and the little wood in the distance.

Mademoiselle Bayard did not much like the island, but she had to put up with it for the whole summer. It was even less like Paris than Stockholm, but she had her duty to do, and she did it. There, in the beautiful bracing air, she still held her deportment classes, and saw that each girl practiced her music a little. But for the rest, they were free to do what they liked, so as to build themselves up for the winter's work.

The governess began her own day with a cup of coffee made from coffee beans carefully transported from Stockholm and ground by herself. The others had glasses of milk and flat bread spread with rich country butter. The peasant woman milked her own cow and made the butter and cheese, though sometimes Jenny was allowed to help her.

On breathlessly hot days, when even the breeze from the sea seemed to fail, they started their dinner with bowls of sour milk sprinkled with sugar. This gave them an appetite and was good for their health as well. There was very seldom meat. Dinner usually consisted of fish and potatoes. And the girls would roam the wood for their dessert, which was often of the pale cloudberries or, later on, the bilberries that ripened when autumn drew near.

Jenny was breathlessly happy. This was her sort of life. The silver birches nodded to welcome her, as they had done long ago when she was a child. But there were no nightingales on the island as there had been in Sollentuna. The only music was that of the distant sea.

"One will really be happy to find oneself back in Stockholm," Mademoiselle Bayard would say, "at least it has lights and shops."

Jenny stared at her in astonishment. "I would like to spend my whole life here. I would prefer it."

The elderly Frenchwoman looked at her curiously. Well she knew what was planned for the girl with the phenomenal voice. "But, my dear, you will become a great singer! There are no opera houses on an island like this. Your days will be spent in the Capital. Perhaps you may even be invited to sing in Copenhagen as well!"

The girl looked at her, startled. "Go out of Sweden? Go abroad?"

"Who knows? If you do well with your lessons from Herr Craelius, you may sing in Paris one day!"

Jenny shook her head decidedly. "I don't want to go to Paris. I won't leave Sweden, ever."

When the day came to return to the mainland, Mademoiselle Bayard welcomed it, but Jenny grew sad. She was brown and healthy now. She loved to plunge into the blue water under the rocks and had learned to swim like a seal. Some of the others said the water was far too cold. But Jenny would splash and sing under the northern sun, which, however, was sinking a little earlier every day, now that autumn was coming.

So presently the piano would be corded again and lifted onto the trolley. The little procession would go down to the landing stage and board the ship once more. And, since the evenings were closing in, the lights of Stockholm would shine over the water to welcome them when they sailed in to Skeppsholmen Harbor.

Jenny's grandmother was dead by now. She missed her visits to her, and no longer went to the Home, or saw the other old ladies sitting beside their checked curtains in their own little corners of the great room. She did not know what had happened to Vasa the cat. No doubt he had died of old age, too.

Now Jenny had begun to lose her awkwardness. She was learning to dance and act as well as to sing. When she had been only a year at the Opera School, she was actually given a small part in a play called *The Polish Mine*. For the opera house put on plays, too, since the Old Dramatic Theater had been burned down some years before.

She was only ten and thrilled at the prospect. The Costume Mistress made her a picturesque little dress, and the Dancing Master made her practice her gestures and movements again and again. She had to dance before the robber chief in a cave; and she had to lure the key to her father's prison from the warder. She found she loved acting as well as singing. Niclas Lind, sitting high up in a cheap seat under the dome, burst with pride as he watched, and told everyone around him who Jenny was.

Afterward, in the taverns he frequented, he would produce his crumpled copy of the *Dagligt Allehanda*, the newspaper which first mentioned Jenny's name. He would read the treasured notice to everyone there, whether they wanted to hear it or not.

" 'Little Jenny Lind,' " he read proudly, " 'acts excellently, we would almost say too well. Such spirit and such theatrical assurance, such utter lack of shyness in a little girl appearing before an audience of twelve hundred people is an exception to the normal course of nature. . . . One thing is certain, that if Jenny Lind continues as she has begun, she will unquestionably be a valuable asset to the Swedish stage.' "

67

It was exactly as her mother had feared. Yet, as Jenny grew older, the stage did not spoil her or change the shyness which, away from the boards, made her life very difficult. It was only when the lights of the opera house went up and the great curtain swung aside, that she became a different person; an enchanting person, graceful and lovely, as if some spell had changed her into another creature.

By the time she was fourteen, she already had sung several small parts in opera. For years, too, she had moved across the great stage as a member of the chorus or in crowds. Every board of it was familiar to her. Now she learned to stand out from the others, lonely yet poised; to let her voice float over the orchestra making knowledgeable members of the audience whisper to one another: "That girl will come to something!"

The last to become reconciled to Jenny's career was, of course, Fru Fellborg. Or rather, Fru Lind as she now consented to be called, since she had become reconciled, too, to Niclas Lind. Perhaps it was their mutual interest in Jenny's career which had drawn them together. Anyway, Niclas now lived in Mäster Samuelsgränd, and Jenny no longer hated the sight of its chocolate door. He brought the place to life with his laughter and jokes.

True, he still tended to disappear for days or weeks at a time. Then his family knew he had once more grown tired of home life and had gone back to his old companions, spending money and getting into debt. When he returned at last, his wife would scold him and the house would become unhappy again for a little. As for his debts, if he could find Jenny first and confess them to her, she generally managed to pay them, somehow, out of her salary. But if she hadn't enough, he was forced to tell his wife.

"It would injure Jenny's career to have her father in a debtor's prison," she would say coldly, handing him the money. "Remember, I do it for her sake, not yours."

He would look a little ashamed for a moment. Then his eyes would twinkle again.

"We shall all be living on Jenny's career someday, won't we? You are right, my dear. It is wise to look to the future!"

Jenny was looking to the future, too. She knew, now, that a good post as opera singer awaited her, and with a good salary attached. Money had never interested her for itself. She did not want fine clothes or jewelry; nor did she envy the delicious creatures, the prima donnas, who owned such things.

Already, at her age, she knew how such luxuries had been obtained.

It was to Amalia that she confided her secret wish.

"As soon as they begin to give me big parts, I shall save and save. Then I'll buy a little cottage in the country for Papa and Mama. Mama likes the country, and Papa won't find the taverns so near."

"But where will you live, Jenny?"

"I shall have to live here in Stockholm during the season. I'll rent a small apartment, and you and I will live in it cozily together. Won't that be fine?"

Amalia gasped with pleasure. "Oh Jenny! I'll do the housework and keep the place spick and span. I'll cook the suppers, and have something hot ready for you when you come back from the opera! I'll mend your dresses and see you buy new ones. You must look fine——"

Jenny interrupted quickly. "I don't want you to slave for me. You've slaved enough already. I love you, Amalia. I want you beside me—always."

That summer she would not go to the island with the others, she would go into the country with Papa and Mama and Amalia. The Opera School didn't mind so long as it was the country, and she rested enough. Already the Linds had taken rooms in a farmhouse, and Jenny was planning to help with the hay. Already she could smell the field flowers and watch the hedgerows growing green and then red with berries. Already she knew that Mama wouldn't be cross any more, because she wouldn't be tired.

The horse-carriage had been ordered to take them there. The morning before they were to leave, Amalia rose from her bed more languidly than usual. She did not touch her breakfast; shivered; grew feverish. They had to fetch a doctor who ordered her back to bed.

"The Fever is rife in Stockholm," he told them gravely. "I am already attending several cases in this street alone."

They put off the carriage and unpacked their boxes again. Jenny was hastily given a bed in the parlor to keep her away from infection. But even from there, she could hear Amalia's delirious voice, going on and on. Then at last, it stopped.

Amalia was dead.

The neighbors stood respectfully by while the funeral procession went past. Jenny bought flowers and more flowers to heap on her sister's grave. Then at last (because the doctor ordered it, and after all, the rooms had to be paid for) they drove out into the country together, three of them, not four.

The long summer days soothed Jenny's hurt. When the time came to cut the hay, she helped to turn it with a pitchfork, and when the big stacks were made, she climbed up them and slid down as she had meant to do.

But she never forgot Amalia.

CHAPTER VI

March 7, 1838.

A gala night at the Opera. They were giving Weber's *Der Freischütz,* and all the tickets were sold out. Not because of the opera itself; it had been performed before and was no novelty. No, the whole city was agog to hear the chief soprano part—the part usually reserved for world-famous singers in their prime—sung by a young girl of seventeen.

Jenny Lind.

Some heads were being shaken. It was a big risk, some people said. A few even said that the Opera Board had gone out of its mind. Not only was the voice part exceedingly trying; how could a young, inexperienced girl act such a dramatic part? Others contradicted them. Had not Jenny's voice melted them before, again and again? Every winter the regular operagoers had seen her, first in tiny, unimportant parts, and then bigger ones. They had grown to love her, to give her a special cheer when she stepped forward to sing. The prophets had all along said Jenny would someday astonish the world. So everyone bought tickets anyway, to see how things would go.

The whole day Jenny scarcely spoke. She was rigid with nerves. Terrified. It even crossed her mind to throw herself on her knees before the Count and beg him to substitute somebody else. She confided her fears to her father.

"Now, Jenny," he admonished her, "recollect you have felt this way before every performance you've appeared in. Every performance."

She was almost crying. "But I've never sung such a big part as this!"

"And so you feel worse. It is always the way with artists. Do I not know them? If a cabbage stood up to sing, believe me it would not stir a leaf. Nor anybody else either."

The thought of a cabbage singing, made her smile weakly. She dried her tears; set her mouth in the obstinate line it still took when she was determined to do something. "If I am to be a great singer, then God will help me. If He does not wish me to be, then He won't."

Jenny had never forgotten her grandmother's lessons. Trust in God, she could hear the old woman say. She grew calmer and went off to the opera house in good time, to let the dresser put on her costume as Agatha and to dust a little rice powder over her face. Rouge she shrank from and never would use.

The sky darkened. The lights over the great portico blazed out. Carriages arrived, a long line of them, and the queues for the cheaper seats grew longer and longer. Presently the musicians hurried in at a side door and began to tune up their instruments. And lastly, when the crowds were already thick, and people on foot had to struggle to reach the great flights of steps, the opera attendants began to push them aside to make way for the occupants of a great gilded coach which had crossed the bridge from the royal palace and was now drawing up.

73

King Karl Johann descended, magnificent in uniform, tall and soldierly as became a former Marshal under Napoleon. Born Jean-Baptiste Bernadotte, the son of a provincial French lawyer, he had been offered the throne of Sweden when the old royal family had died out. He had won the love and respect of his people. They felt he was a worthy successor to their great soldier-kings, Gustavus Adolphus and Charles XII.

The King turned to give his hand to Queen Desideria, born plain Désirée Cléry. She was not a strong character like himself, but a simple soul who tried hard to support her husband. In youth, she had been pretty enough to enslave the young Napoleon, then but a shabby officer with no future before him. For that reason, Monsieur Cléry, the prosperous silk merchant of Marseilles, had frowned on their engagement. Surely his daughter could do better than that!

But now his daughter, Désirée, was actually Queen of Sweden. And his other daughter, Julie, who had insisted upon marrying young Napoleon Bonaparte's eldest brother, had become Queen of Spain.

Queen Desideria wore the old court dress of Sweden. A black gown, perfect for showing off jewels, with little puffed sleeves of white slashed with black. Tonight the dress was of velvet because the winds from the Baltic blew cold. A diamond coronet gleamed in her still-dark hair. Emeralds clasped her throat and arms. She drew her white ermine cape more closely about her as she ascended the steps on her husband's arm, bowing graciously to the people who stood around.

The Royal Box was all crimson and gold. As soon as they had taken their places, the lamps were dimmed and the orchestra broke into the well-known overture which had entranced a first-night audience in Paris seventeen years before. Then the red velvet curtain twitched, moved slowly upward and disclosed the first scene, laid among the forests of Bohemia and placed in the Middle Ages.

It is the story of a sharpshooting contest, the winner to be rewarded with the hand of Agatha, daughter of the Head Ranger to the Duke of Bohemia. Unsuccessful at first, Agatha's lover accepts seven magical bullets, warranted to hit any mark. But they are the gift of the Devil, and Agatha's lover must promise his soul in exchange. Only the Devil himself knows that the seventh bullet is still his to command.

The forest scenery was magnificently painted; the male singers in the First Act all sang well. But the audience was restive. It was the Second Act they wanted, the act where Jenny was to appear. When the lights went up again, a buzz of anticipation went through the auditorium. Even Jenny, waiting behind the wings, could hear it, and it deepened her feeling of sickness and fright.

The Count himself stood beside her, trying to reassure her. He was troubled and agitated, too, although no trace of this showed in his long, aristocratic countenance. He wore an Order across his breast, for was this not a royal occasion? But, looking at Jenny, he now feared the occasion might turn into a fiasco. He had

75

never seen her look so frightened; so plain. "Why the devil hasn't she colored her lips at least?" he asked himself irritably.

But now the orchestra was playing again. It was her cue. And with that cue, she suddenly became another person; became Agatha, waiting in her own little room for news of her lover's success. So the curtain rose slowly upon her. She was Agatha herself, in her pallor and agitation. But as that pure, thrilling voice soared out over the footlights, she was Jenny Lind, too.

There was not a rustle or movement in the opera house now. She held them spellbound. They forgot they were watching the debut of a young girl whose progress they had followed for years. They were watching Agatha's passionate excitement at the approach of her lover and experienced with her all the fears and forebodings that rose in her as she learned of his intention to go to the haunted Wolf's Glen.

She was still Agatha when the curtain fell. She scarcely heard the message conveyed by a footman, first to the Count and then by him to her. The King and Queen bade her come to their Box. She followed the Count in a dream, down the curving back passages, toward the baize-lined door leading into the Box. It was like another little stage, for all eyes were turned to her as she stepped inside and curtseyed mechanically to the tall King and the kindly woman in black velvet and emeralds.

She scarcely heard the compliments they paid her. But she saw the Queen's eyes were red and that she held a damp little handkerchief squeezed in the palm of one hand.

"Mademoiselle Lind, I trust you are not going to wring our hearts in the last act, as you have done already."

The words were spoken in broken Swedish, for Desideria had never mastered the language as her husband had done. But the tears in her eyes spoke for her. Jenny said simply, "I cannot help it, your Majesty. Agatha suffers, and I suffer with her."

Then the Count was leading her back again, behind the great curtain about to rise on the last scene. The glittering audience turned its opera glasses away from the Royal Box and concentrated once more on the stage. Now Agatha is seen in the forest, dressed as a bride, watching the contest, praying for Max's success. Now the Duke orders Max, with his last bullet, to shoot at a dove flying through the trees. But the Devil has power over that bullet. Agatha shrieks and falls. . . .

When the curtain comes down for the last time, the whole opera house is in a tumult. The audience, at first struck dumb by the horror conveyed by Jenny's acting and singing, now bursts into a tumult of sound. Men stand on their seats to clap. Some women are in hysterics. Louder and louder the roar of sound penetrates to the wings where Jenny stands, half-fainting with fatigue, clinging to the Count's arm.

"You must go before the curtain!" he orders and drags her forward. The footlight candles waver before the red folds. He pushes the curtain aside and leads her forward, still in her bridal dress and veil, still clutching the bouquet of artificial flowers.

"Curtsey first to the Royal Box!" He hisses into her ear.

She has just presence of mind enough to do as he says. The Queen has risen, is leaning forward. She has thrown her own bouquet of hothouse flowers, where it falls at Jenny's feet. The small figure in white picks it up, dropping the other bouquet, and, curtseying again, holds it instead. Once more the audience roars its applause. . . .

Only when she has retired to her dressing room does the Count allow himself to relax. Then he passes a handkerchief over his brow; draws a deep breath. The dangerous experiment has succeeded. A new Prima Donna is born.

Niclas Lind was in the dressing room waiting for her, Jenny fell into his arms. "Did you like it, Papa? Did I do well?"

"How do I know, my darling? I wasn't there."

"Not there?" Surprise shook her out of her numbed exhaustion. "But—but I told them to send you and Mama tickets. To send the best in the House!"

"Oh, your mama was there all right. But I—I was too frightened for you, Jenny. I didn't dare——"

"What did you do?"

"Walked around and around the opera house and tried to judge from the cheers how it had gone. *They* reassured me all right. Don't laugh at your old papa. If you had seen him a few minutes ago, hanging about the steps trying to hear what everyone was saying as they went down them!"

"What did they say?" she faltered.

"What do you think? They've never heard a voice like yours before, Jenny. And they never will, either. Now come home and get to bed. That's what you need."

That night, by her bedside, Jenny fell on her knees and thanked God for his wonderful gift. She always remembered that night. For the rest of her life she observed the seventh of March as a sacred day. She called it her second birthday, and used to asked her friends to pray for her then. Long, long afterward, she said to a friend, "I got up that morning one person, and went to bed another."

The newspapers were full of her, next morning. There was nothing but ecstatic praise. The Directors of the Opera felt they should mark the occasion. So, a few days later, a deputation called to present her with a pair of lyre-shaped silver candlesticks. They were engraved with the words: "In remembrance of the 7th March."

She kept the candlesticks all her life.

CHAPTER VII

Jenny was now the rage of Stockholm.

Hostesses fought to have her at their receptions. Her salary was raised, but it was still little enough—about £60 a year, with a bonus for each performance. She was still quite uninterested in dress, and had her plain white gowns made by a dressmaker who needed the money and whom she wished to help.

Her mother was half annoyed at this, half grateful. Annoyed because Jenny could scarcely make a proper appearance in the fine houses she was bidden to; grateful that most of the money was still handed over to her, to help with the housekeeping. The school had petered out. She felt that she needed it.

Jenny stood before the long glass in her dressmaker's room, while the woman pinned up the material for the new dress she was to wear at a musical party. Jenny had a very slim waist, and the material was to be rucked and gathered into a large rosette of the material.

"A cluster of rosebuds now, would Miss Lind not prefer that?"

The dressmaker spoke through a mouthful of pins in the wonderful way dressmakers have. Jenny shook her head. "No ornaments, please. Just a plain knot or something, to gather in the folds. I hate feeling dressed-up when I'm singing."

"Louise!" the woman called out, "bring me more pins."

Louise Johanson hurried through with the pins from the workroom beyond. Jenny smiled at her old companion, then looked at her more sharply. The gentle, quiet girl had always reminded her of Amalia. Even now, that remembrance brought a pang, as she stood there watching Louise hand the pins where her mistress required them. How differently fate had dealt with the three of them! She on the crest of the wave, while Louise stood serving, and Amalia was dead.

"You are looking very tired, Louise," Jenny said, "and you have dark smudges under your eyes, too. When summer comes, I hope you can get away into the country."

Louise shook her head. "I don't think I can afford a holiday this year. I have to find new lodgings, and who knows what that will cost?"

The dressmaker put in briskly: "She sleeps in a mere cupboard of a room as it is. Imagine, Miss Lind, no window! It is I who insist upon her changing her lodgings. Already she has a cough."

Jenny opened her mouth, then shut it again. How dreadful not to have enough money oneself to help an old friend! But her father had got into one of his scrapes, and she had paid everything she had to get him out of it. And the next quarter's salary wasn't due till the end of the month.

Always this trouble about money! Her mother talked of it incessantly, even though they were better off now than they had ever been before. But Fru Lind had grown avaricious. She was constantly urging Jenny to ask for larger fees for her performances, and this Jenny was reluctant to do. Had not the Opera School made her what she was? She felt she had scarcely repaid her debt to them.

Louise delivered the parcel with the new dress. It came just in time for Jenny to put it on to go to the fashionable evening party which closed the season. "Have you found a new room?" she asked as she took the parcel in at the door.

The girl shook her head. "They all ask too much."

Jenny stood in the tiny hallway, deep in thought after Louise had gone. Her mother came out and said sharply, "Are you not dressing yet? Make haste! The Baroness' carriage is being sent for you. It will come any minute."

That hard, lecturing voice had become intolerable. It put Jenny in the wrong key for any occasion before her. She retreated quickly into the little parlor which was now her bedroom. The piano was there anyway, so she could practice when she wanted to. The marble table now bore a looking glass and she sat down before it to arrange her hair.

Amalia's face seemed to look over her own shoulder, reflecting itself in the glass. Amalia's voice seemed to say, "Do something for her, as if it was me!"

Jenny began to arrange her hair hurriedly, so as to have a word with her mother before she went out. She wore her hair, at this time, in glossy curls on each side of her face. The hair itself gleamed with brushing, but the curls had to be made over her finger. It took time. Then she slipped on the dress, snatched up the white cashmere shawl which had been her one extravagance this season, and went into the kitchen.

"Mama, have you any money left from the last amount I gave you?"

"Certainly not! You forget that bill from your father's tailor. Of course I had to pay it as usual."

Just then there came a thundering knock at the door. The Baroness' footman was summoning her down to the carriage. Although such thoughts were not usual with Jenny, it passed through her mind that the man must be astonished as well as scornful at finding one of his mistress' guests in such a humble abode.

By now Amalia and I might have been living together in a little apartment, far from Mäster Samuelsgränd! she thought to herself as she followed him down the dark stairs.

The party was in one of the nobles' palaces in the center of the old town. She passed up the marble stairway, after handing her shawl to a servant. Two great drawing rooms had been thrown together into one for tonight. The doors stood open into the upper hall to let a current of air into the crowded room. She saw the glitter of jewels and uniforms even before she entered it. Then she stepped over the threshold, a small, shy figure, not wearing even one jewel or one flower. And the noise of conversation suddenly hushed. Everyone looked toward her.

She curtseyed to her host and hostess. She was accustomed, now, to such splendid gatherings, but she did not—and never did—feel at ease in a crowd. Faces appeared and bowed before her. Then came the moment for which everyone had been waiting. The Baroness led her toward the piano.

"Will you consent to charm us with some music, Miss Lind?"

She sat down at the piano, let her eyes roam through the crowd, seeking a friendly, not merely an admiring, face. There they were, Adolf Lindbad the famous composer and his wife, Sophie. They belonged to *her* world. Adolf caught her eye and gave her a nod of greeting. She would sing some of his songs.

She was a good pianist and accompanied herself beautifully. The songs seemed simple, but were intricate to sing. They were set to Swedish words which usually touched her heart. But tonight she almost sang them mechanically, for Amalia's face seemed to look out at her from the flames of the candles lighting the keyboard.

However, nobody seemed to notice any difference. There was the usual outburst of applause when she had finished. People came up to be introduced to her and she forgot everything in the effort to speak to them. But as usual, it became less and less of an effort. Where compliments were meant, and kind, she responded warmly and humbly. Her face reflected each thought so that the plain features melted and she became once more beautiful, as when she was singing. She fascinated the whole company; she was real, was as natural as the Swedish landscape itself. It was not often that the elegant creatures present this evening came upon anybody quite natural and unspoiled.

Her sense of fun revived, too. A gushing *grande dame* who pressed her hand, said, "Dear Miss Lind, I was transported, absolutely transported, by your performance in *Roberto* last week. Tell me, when you clung to the Cross, what dreadful thoughts passed through your mind?"

An unexpected dimple showed in Jenny's cheek. "I believe," she answered demurely, "I was planning how to trim my new bonnet."

It wasn't true of course. When somebody else, on another occasion, asked without affectation how she managed to sing that song so wonderfully—the song in which she strives to save her foster brother from the Devil, she answered, "How can I tell? I stood at the man's right hand, and the Fiend at his left, and all I could think of was, how to save him."

But Jenny had always detested false compliments and affectation.

Now, at last, she was free to join her true friends. She crossed over to where the Lindbads sat. Sophie greeted her warmly, but Adolf, who had risen at her approach, bent over her hand and said in a low voice, "What is the matter with you tonight, Jenny? You didn't sing as you usually do. And I don't say that because you happened to sing my songs!"

She gazed, startled, up at his face. "Did—did anybody else notice?"

"Of course not. What does this crowd know of music! Your *voice* was as wonderful as usual. But your spirit was somewhere else."

She knew it was true. Her spirit had been with Amalia. Louise had put Amalia into her mind so strongly, she felt there was a purpose behind this absorption which had prevented her losing herself in the songs.

Nobody else seemed to have seen any difference in her singing tonight. She was loaded with praise; taken downstairs on the arm of her host, as the most important person present, and seated at a supper table heaped with roses and glittering with massive silver. As usual she ate the plainest things she could see. Afterward, there was dancing. Jenny had learned to love it. She danced as lightly as thistledown. She once more managed to forget Amalia.

The carriage drove her back home, along the darkened streets past the silent houses. She refused to let the footman escort her upstairs, but climbed the three flights by the light of the oil lamp which swung from the ceiling, carefully keeping her new dress from touching the dusty banisters. She knocked on the chocolate door, and her mother, who had been waiting up half the night, let her in.

Cinderella had come home.

Fru Lind was yawning and worn out with tiredness. Jenny tried to apologize for keeping her up so long, and bent forward to kiss her. But Fru Lind turned her cheek away so quickly, the kiss turned into a peck.

"You have enjoyed yourself with your fine friends I suppose? Well, it is all good advertisement, so I mustn't grumble. If only you would be sensible and ask for more money, we might even keep a little servant to open the door!"

Jenny tried to laugh. "Where would she sleep?"

"Oh, in the box-room. There's quite a good window there, and I could easily clear the stuff in it."

"So there is!" Jenny seemed startled for a moment.

Her mother noticed it and felt triumphant. "Where there's a will there's a way! Now, perhaps you'll do as I ask you, and see to it that we don't have to save and pinch and live any more like this!"

Next morning Jenny got up and joined her mother in the kitchen. Fru Lind had been up long ago and had finished most of the housework already. One of the small luxuries they could now afford was to drink coffee every day. Jenny dipped her roll into the fragrant coffee, sucked a corner of it as she used to do when she was a child at Sollentuna, and said, "Mama, I've been thinking. About what you said last night."

"Eh?" Fru Lind paused as she peeled the potaoes for dinner. Her face lit up at the thought that perhaps Jenny would consent to earn more money at last. Jenny saw the thought and blocked it at once.

"Not," she said firmly, "about asking the Directors to increase my bonus. They've supported me for eight years without my bringing them in a penny. Until they've got more of their money back, it wouldn't be fair."

"Well?" Her mother had gone back, disappointedly, to the potatoes.

"It's the box-room. If it was cleared as you said, we could put a lodger there. It wouldn't pay us enough to keep a servant"—Jenny smiled to herself at the thought, and the dimple showed in her cheek again—"but you could have a woman in to do the scrubbing, perhaps."

"That's true. Why hadn't I thought of it before!" Fru Lind let the potato knife splash back into the basin, retrieved it, and went on. "Not that I'd waste the money on some worthless woman who would only drink it up in beer! But it would be something extra."

Then another thought chased the first. "We'd have to be particular who we took in. No students. I know those students, they are just as fond of beer as anyone else."

"Louise Johanson is looking for a room. She's quiet, and she goes out to work every day."

So Louise came back to live with the Linds. Jenny had helped her mother to scrub and clean out the tiny room which no one had thought of using before. All the pickle jars were moved from the floor and put up on a shelf in the kitchen. The boxes were stored under the big bed in Fru Lind's room. The small window was polished until it shone. It gave a view of the roofs in the neighborhood and looked down on a gay window box farther along the street.

Out of her own money, Jenny bought a striped woven rug for the floor. The one possession her grandmother had had to leave them—a good chest of drawers—was polished too. Jenny tacked up gay curtains, and moved in the trundle bed she had slept in herself, as a child. When Louise saw it, she was delighted.

"Of course," Fru Lind said, "we must ask a good rent."

Jenny put down her foot again. "We shall ask Louise what she can afford to give. Not a penny more."

And her mother had to agree.

CHAPTER VIII

The lake had a marble rim instead of sedge. Statues mirrored themselves in it instead of birch trees. Behind the lake stretched a formal terrace instead of green fields; and behind that again, the Summer Palace of Drottningholm.

It was not real country, as Jenny understood it. Yet it was in the heart of the countryside, many miles from Stockholm. The royal carriage which had fetched her here, set her down near the terrace. A lady in waiting came forward to greet her and lead her indoors. The stone nymphs paid no attention to either of them but continued to stare at nothing across the lake.

"Her Majesty is longing to meet and talk with you," the lady in waiting said kindly. She was wearing the old court dress of black with white sleeves. But, because it was summer and daytime, the dress was filmy and the sleeves slashed with black silk ribbons.

Jenny smiled shyly and entered the palace. She refused to be awed by the magnificent painted ceilings, the chandeliers high up in the roof like Christmas trees. Now they had reached a white doorway. A footman clad in the familiar scarlet and gold of the opera attendants (for they too, were in royal service) threw the door open.

The lady in waiting advanced a few steps ahead of Jenny into the room, curtseyed, and announced, "Your

Majesty, here is Fröken Jenny Lind!"

When Jenny straightened up after her own curtsey, she saw Queen Desideria had risen from her sofa and come forward to greet her.

"Norma—Alice—Agatha—How many names you have, dear Miss Lind! I have seen you in every rôle. I invited you here to play the part of yourself."

The French Queen stumbled over the Swedish words, making mistakes even in that one simple compliment, so that Jenny herself gained courage. She felt her hand taken and she was led gently toward the ornate and splendid sofa upon which the Queen had been sitting.

"You know, I was passionately fond of music myself. I was actually practicing a duet with my sister Julie when they told me Jean-Baptiste—that my husband was now King and I, Queen. So I closed the lid of the piano and have never touched it since."

She sighed, but gave no reason for this. Jenny's curiosity was aroused. "But why, Ma'am? Why should the Queen of Sweden not play the piano?"

The plump, homely woman gazed at her earnestly. "Because I detest flattery. They would have flattered me to death about my playing. To my face, that is. But behind my back——Well, I confess I was quite a good musician. Yet they would only say I played well enough for a queen!"

She led Jenny toward the piano presently, and asked her to sing. The windows were open toward the lake, and the statues down below seemed frozen into listening attitudes when that miraculous voice floated out to them. After a few Swedish songs and arias from favorite operas, the Queen allowed herself to ask in wistful tones, "Can you sing something French? You know I am a Frenchwoman still, at heart!"

So Jenny sang some sugarplum songs which, to her, seemed tinsel, but even when pronounced in her bad French, seemed to touch Désirée's heart. They were what Niclas called Café songs, and they had been the rage of the Paris Desideria knew many years ago. Her father used to hum them to his guitar, and they came back to Jenny now. But she only sang them with her voice, not her heart. And she stopped as soon as possible. The Queen, disappointed but polite, supposed she was beginning to tire.

"Yes, they bring Paris back to me! Yet you know, I belong to far farther south; to Marseilles and the Mediterranean. When I spent my first year in Paris after marrying, I thought I would die of the cold!"

Jenny laughed. "A good preparation for the greater Swedish cold, your Majesty!"

But Desideria still looked pensive. "How strange it is! Once I thought Paris unendurable, it was so different— so far from home. Now I think of it fondly because at least——But I am chattering nonsense, while you are probably tired and starving after the long drive from Stockholm and the music you have made. . . ." She picked up a small silver bell from the table beside her and rang it. Instantly the lady in waiting who had first received Jenny appeared again.

"Will you take Miss Lind to her apartments and let her know when we dine?"

Because of the distance between the summer palace

91

and Stockholm, Jenny had been invited to stay the night. She had brought no maid with her because she had none. It had crossed her mind to invite Louise Johanson to come in that capacity. But Louise was often kept late in the workshop; and besides, she hesitated to place the girl in the position of serving her, just because Louise was her mother's lodger.

So she arranged her hair and dressed herself. As she fastened the simple white dress Louise had helped to make, she smiled once more, at the Queen's near-slip when she spoke of her fondness for Paris. Desideria had been going to say that she had learned to appreciate Paris after the cold provincialism of Stockholm. It was well known that she had never taken to Sweden and had, indeed, lingered on in Paris long after her husband had taken up residence in his new kingdom.

This palace was in the French taste, and that taste repelled Jenny as much as it charmed the Queen. All was marble and cold formality. Although it was in the depths of the country, there was nothing about it to remind Jenny of the real Swedish countryside; only artificial fountains instead of streams, parterres of bedded-out plants instead of wild flowers, and the stately rhythm of old court life as laid down by the former kings of Sweden. This, King Karl Johann thought it wise to adhere to. The French soldier who had risen to a crown knew better than to destroy the etiquette supporting that crown.

So on the whole, Jenny was glad to escape back to her own life next day. She had another audience with Desideria who sent for her to say good-by. The Queen drew her toward her and kissed her affectionately.

"Accept this with my thanks for your superlative singing last night!" She placed in her hand a small box containing a brooch made of pearls and diamonds. The pearls outlined the shape of a delicate Swedish anemone, and the diamonds lay on its half-opened petals like dew.

"I have always observed that you wear no jewelry. But this is a simple flower. Perhaps you will wear it sometimes, for my sake?"

When Jenny reached home again and showed her mother the brooch, Fru Lind looked scornfully at it. "She might have given you one all in diamonds when she was about it! Is that a fit present from a Queen?"

Jenny flushed angrily. She bit her lips and forced herself to remain silent a moment or two. Then she said, "The Queen gave me something she knew I would wear. She gave me consideration along with the brooch."

Louise picked it up and held it against the white folds around Jenny's shoulders. "It represents you to perfection!"

It seemed they were all on edge after the long, dark winter. Even Louise did not seem as contented as usual, and when Jenny asked where she was going to take her holiday, she said rather shortly that she did not intend to leave Stockholm at all. Her employer was going off on a round of visits to country houses where a dressmaker was made welcome during the summer. Louise had, it seemed, promised to make a few dresses cheaply for customers who, like herself, were not going to leave the capital.

Jenny could not alter this arrangement, but she could not approve, either. Louise was again looking pale and ill. The board Jenny arranged she should pay to Fru Lind should have left enough from her salary to indulge in a proper holiday. But when Jenny said anything, Louise only told her quickly she could not afford it; and she refused, too, any loan or present from the other girl.

Jenny went off on her own holiday, vaguely uneasy. Had her mother's avarice and penny-pinching already infected Louise?

She tried to forget all her worries, in the long, glorious days, far from the city. She visited the little university town of Uppsala, along with her friends the Lindbads. The students serenaded her during a torchlight procession, and the Students' Song was bawled under her window again and again. She had just been having supper with an old friend of the Lindbads', and they had eaten the Swedish version of yoghurt—the sour milk Fru Ferndal had given her long ago—from a large washbasin because the supper party was hurriedly got together and there really wasn't enough china and cutlery, which made it all the more fun.

Uppsala wasn't quite the country, but Jenny enjoyed herself all the same. Her friends the Lindbads noticed, however, that a shade came over her face at the thought of returning to Stockholm. And they guessed it was caused by more than her dislike of a city.

As they finished the yoghurt, Sophie Lindbad ventured to touch on the subject no one had uttered before.

"Jenny, dearest, confess to your old friends. You are not happy at home."

"I have never been happy at home," Jenny answered quietly.

"Your mother has an impossible temper. Just now, you are young enough to throw off its effects. Even so, there are nights when you sing better than others. You cannot afford to live near such discord." It was Adolf Lindbad who spoke now.

Jenny remained silent for some time. Then she said, "I have no right to leave my parents. You know that. Don't blame Mother too much. She has had such a hard life! And she can't throw things off as my father can."

"You think it is your duty to stay where you are," Adolf warned her, "but remember, you have a duty too, to your art."

His wife Sophie added, with a kind glance toward the silent girl, "Remember too, if things ever get too bad, you can always find a home with us."

Many a time, after Jenny returned to Stockholm, she thought of these words. Niclas Lind had gone off with friends on a jolly boating party along the coast. His wife, more than ever fretful through remaining in Stockholm in the heat, scolded Jenny and Louise impartially. Jenny feared Louise would go. She was sure she only remained because of the low rent.

Long before the rest of Stockholm returned to its homes, the opera house began work again. Jenny was to appear in different rôles twice weekly during the forthcoming season. As well as that, she had accepted invitations to sing at concerts, and to take the principal part in two oratorios; Haydn's *Creation,* and Mendelssohn's *St. Paul.* Young and strong though she was, she would drag herself home, exhausted, after each rehearsal. And if Niclas wasn't at home to take the edge off things, she could scarcely bear the continual grumbles and demands for money which met her each evening, as soon as she crossed the doorstep.

God grant me patience to bear it! She would stand in the middle of her room, staring at the closed piano, dreading when she must step into the kitchen to face the others at supper. If her father were there, things went better. But she sensed that Louise was just as unhappy under that roof as she was herself.

The season began. It opened with a gay opera, *The Daughter of the Regiment* by Donizetti. In it, Jenny laughed and sang lightheartedly. Although she could wring your heart in sad pieces, she loved comedy parts, too. They were a relief from tragedies which tore her to pieces and left her exhausted.

This was followed, later in the season, by *Robert le Diable,* one of Jenny's most successful parts. The dress rehearsal took most of the day. She had just time to hurry back to Mäster Samuelsgränd in the late afternoon, so as to have a short rest and a little refreshment before returning to the opera house in time to dress for the first act.

Humming a little tune from the opera, she ran upstairs more softly and swiftly than usual. The front door was not fastened properly, so she needed merely to push it open to enter the flat. Nobody heard her entrance. She heard sounds coming from the kitchen. Louise's voice, low and tremulous. Then her mother's loud and angry.

"You know the sum Jenny mentioned was quite ridiculous!"

"I've paid you more already. Please, please let me stay!"

"Even now it is the cheapest room in Stockholm. If you wish to stay here, you must pay accordingly."

Jenny threw open the kitchen door and marched into the room. "Mama, are you raising Louise's rent?"

"You have no right to interfere if I do," her mother told her angrily.

"Excuse me, I think I have. Louise came here because I assured her the rent would be what she could afford to pay. We fixed it at ten *Riksdaler*, did we not?" She looked inquiringly at the girl who nodded.

"Have you been paying more already?"

Louise looked frightened and did not answer. Fru Lind answered sullenly for her. "She has been paying fifteen *Riksdaler* while you were in the country. And little enough at that!"

"And now you ask for yet more! More for a room you never thought of renting at all till I put the idea in your mind, to help Louise. For shame, Mother!"

Her mother grew angrier still. "If she doesn't want to pay more she can leave. Yes, and you, too!" she shouted.

Jenny grew very pale. She looked at her mother a moment, then gestured to Louise to follow her into her own room. She shut the door carefully. The two girls, shaken, remained silent. There on the marble table, stood the glass of milk, which Jenny always drank before a performance. She did not touch it.

"Louise, forgive us!" she said in a low voice.

The other took a step forward eagerly. "I understand! I know it is not *you* who would do such a thing. Just to be near you, I would be willing to try to scrape up the extra money. She asks now twenty *Riksdaler* a week. . . ."

"And you have been paying fifteen already! Was that why you couldn't afford to take a holiday?"

Louise nodded dumbly. Jenny went over to her dressing table, picked up her hairbrush and turned it over as if examining the bristles. She was making up her mind. Presently she half-turned and said, "I have come to an end. If I tell Mother now that I am going to obey her and leave the house, there will be another storm. And there mustn't be any more. I can't stand them. Listen, Louise. I'm going to ask you to do something."

"Anything!"

"Mother is going to the opera tonight. I gave her a ticket. That means the flat will be empty. Will you pack all our things, yours and mine, and take them away in a cab?"

"Where to?" Louise gaped at her. Jenny was scribbling on a piece of paper.

"To this address. Here's money for the cab. They are two kind elderly women who will take us in. They will let you have a room for as long as you like. I saw you were unhappy here so I asked them."

"You mean—we go there tonight?"

Jenny shood her head. "Better wait till tomorrow morning. After breakfast, I'll tell Mama we are obeying her orders and leaving. I've got to wait till the performance is over anyway. And there's no sense in having a row in the middle of the night."

"You too, Jenny? You really mean to leave, too?"

Jenny's lips set tightly. "You heard what she said. I've had enough. Some good friends of mine once offered me a home with them. I'm ready now, to accept their offer."

CHAPTER IX

So Jenny went to live with Adolf and Sophie Lindbad. They were a charming and devoted couple. Adolf was handsome and talented. He had already made a name for himself in the Stockholm musical world by his delightful songs. Sophie and Jenny had become fast friends some time before; and Jenny often sang Adolf's songs at her concerts. They lived in a wing of the old Bondy Palace and entertained all sorts of interesting people. Jenny was very happy there.

She sang brilliantly that season. Her whole soul seemed to be in the parts she played. The audiences laughed and sighed with her, or were transfixed with grief if she wanted them to be. Never had an opera soprano matched such a ravishing voice with such wonderful acting. It was the loveliest voice Stockholm had ever heard. People said her roulades and trills were like pearls, perfectly matched, even and soft. She sang like a bird. It was then the newspapers gave her the name that would always be hers.

The Swedish Nightingale.

All her interpretations were new. Nobody knew just how she would render each well-worn part. She refused to follow the tricks of other singers. How could she, when she insisted that one must feel the part for oneself?

"I scarcely ever think of the effect I am producing," she said to somebody once, "and if the thought does sometimes cross my mind, it spoils my acting. It seems to me when I act that I feel fully all the emotions of the character I represent. I fancy myself—indeed believe myself—to be in her situtation, and I never think of the audience."

That was only possible of course, because of the great technique she had worked so hard at, since she was nine. She could forget technique both in singing and acting, because it was there. In *La Sonnambula,* for instance, the stage of that time was cluttered with scenery for the great sleepwalking scene. Rocks, paths, rivulets, meandered all over it. With other prima donnas, it was the custom to mark out with chalk the route the heroine must take, so that she could cast her eyes down and follow it safely even though appearing to walk in her sleep.

But Jenny would have no chalk lines. She refused to act that scene with her eyes on the ground. She knew no real sleepwalker did so. Nightly she froze the audiences in their seats as she came on, eyes fixed and unseeing, staring blindly in front of her.

A foppish young man sat in the stalls watching her one night. He had crossed over from Copenhagen specially to see this new star everyone was raving over. But he was no stranger to Stockholm either, for his wife had come from there. He was a dancer, and had learned his trade in Paris, from Vestris and Taglioni. Now, in charge of the famous ballet company of Copenhagen, he alone of all the dancers in Europe, maintained the old school of polished, courtly performance.

When Jenny began her slow, faltering advance toward

the footlights, August Bournonville put up his single eyeglass and studied her acting from the professional point of view.

"Amazing for a girl of eighteen!" he said to himself. As she sang, her voice magnetized him, so that he could scarcely note the magnificent acting which did not appear to be acting, but life. She was real, this sleepwalker. And even in her hesitating, groping walk, he discerned the grace he tried to inculcate into his dancers.

How she would electrify his own theater at home! Perhaps, someday. . . . He dropped his eyeglass again, as the curtain fell and the lights went up. He left his seat and penetrated through to the back of the auditorium. The murmur of his own name, August Bournonville, was enough. He was as famous in his way as Jenny was in hers. Even the Count, watchful in the wings as usual, came forward, bowing to greet him.

"Mademoiselle Lind? She is in her dressing room where she generally likes to remain undisturbed. But I will see——"

Jenny turned around at the tap on the door. She was pale and exhausted now, for the sleepwalking scene always tried her to the utmost. But she greeted the stranger with her usual grave politeness, and became more animated as soon as the Count explained who Bournonville was. Here was another artist like herself. His compliments were sincere, and based on knowledge.

Also, he spoke Swedish with a slight French accent, which endeared him to her further. He was, of course, French by extraction, and had spent many years in Paris besides. The way he pronounced his words recalled both

Queen Desideria and old Mademoiselle Bayard.

"Such a voice as yours, Mademoiselle, should be heard farther afield. I have never heard anything to equal it, even in the Paris Opera House. You are not planning to sing in Paris?"

"Don't tempt our Star away from us!" the Count put in with a smile.

Bournonville said brusquely, "And why not? Would she not bring glory to Stockholm by doing so?"

Jenny shrugged her shoulders slightly. Much as she loved a French accent because it reminded her of two people she cared for and admired, the thought of Paris repelled rather than attracted her. The French were a light-minded people, and she had always heard that their morals were distressing. But it was only talk after all.

She said, "There are very fine singers there, I believe. I would not dare to compete with them."

"Yes, there are some magnificent voices, trained by Garcia, who lives there. You have heard of Manuel Garcia I suppose? The greatest teacher of *bel canto* in the world!"

"Here," said the Count coldly, "we also teach the Italian style of singing."

Bournonville knew Jenny was a product of the Stockholm school. He hastened to say, "Mademoiselle Lind is a finer singer than any singing in Paris just now, I assure you!"

"Yes," said Jenny quietly, "I have heard of Garcia of course. As for my voice being finer, God gave it to me. I have nothing to do with that."

But after her two visitors had gone she remained thoughtful. Manuel Garcia . . . *Bel canto* singing had certainly been taught her from the first; but the style had traveled a long way from Italy! Each season a guest singer had come from there to sing opposite her; a tenor or baritone. Their style of singing was impeccable. Her own voice was of such a marvelous quality, most people listened to it with uncritical delight. Her trills were flawless; she could sing the highest notes pianissimo instead of screeching them, and then glide down the scale in semi-tones like a ripple of water.

But . . . was not her breath control difficult at times? It was *that* which she envied in the French- and Italian-trained singers. They could hold a long note effortlessly, by the use of some technique she had not yet learned. And what about the slight huskiness at the end of each season, which as yet nobody noticed but herself?

Paris. City of noise and frivolity. City of fashion and falseness. She might love Désirée and Mademoiselle Bayard, but the thought of such a sinful city revolted her.

That season she met for the first time the Italian baritone, Giovanni Belletti. He was dark and handsome, and he sang opposite her in romantic rôles. Soon a new warmth came into his voice when he sang love songs to her. She knew the symptoms. She liked him, but that was all.

It was the same with the other young men who fell passionately in love with her. The plain little girl had developed an allure nobody would have dreamed of a few years ago. It was her amazing simplicity and sincerity which drew them. She could not help it. But, equally, she could not love them back.

As Phineas Barnum, the showman, said of her long afterwards, and when he knew her better: "It is a mistake to say that the fame of Jenny Lind rests solely upon her ability to sing. She was a woman who would be adored if she had had the voice of a crow."

Now the days were getting longer again, and her heavy winter programme was nearing its end. She had returned, this evening, to the Lindbads', thinking only of a light supper and bed. But the drawing room was lit up, the stove was roaring, and there were people there, surely, for she heard voices as she opened the door, and her heart sank.

Thank goodness, it was only Belletti! He had got there before her, and was munching an open sandwich unromantically filled with smoked salmon. Adolf was talking to him, while Sophie, elegant and graceful, sat doing embroidery. So it wasn't a party after all.

She sat down wearily on the chair beside Sophie. "Did it go well?"

They both assured her she had been dynamic. "You held that audience in the hollow of your hand." Adolf helped himself to a sandwich, too, adding, "As usual."

With a rare touch of impatience, she said, "I'm not asking for compliments. My voice is tired. I know it."

Belletti threw her a dark glance over the table. "Your acting was superb. Even I, who am hardened to acting, was swept away by it, as I always am. Take care, Jenny! Some night you will make me forget my own part!"

"Oh, my acting! That's easy. I simply think myself

into it. The author of the libretto has written it for me. I only have to live it for an hour or two. I was talking about my voice."

"Perfect. A wonder-voice."

"My singing technique then." She sounded more impatient still. The others glanced at her in surprise. Sophie shrugged her shoulders, then bent over her needle again. Poor child, she is tired!

"Here is your glass of milk, Jenny." Adolf's own voice was fatherly, concerned. "There's something hot for you in that little covered dish as well. Remember, you haven't eaten since midday."

It was true. Like most singers, Jenny ate lightly on the day of a performance and her supper after it. As she sipped her milk, she looked across at Belletti who was adoring her with his eyes. Would that adoration make him speak the truth, or otherwise?

"Tell me about Manuel Garcia," she said deliberately. "You have heard our singers who were trained by Herr Craelius. You've heard me. Was his training in *bel canto* the equal of Garcia's?"

There was a long pause. Then Belletti shook his head.

Sophie laid down her embroidery. "Enough of music for tonight! Soon, Jenny, you will get your holidays. Then you will feel more rested."

But Jenny remained thoughtful. Presently she went up to her room. She stared at her reflection as she brushed her hair in the mirror. Her salary had been raised again. She gave a great deal of it away. But still, she could save. . . .

The King had paid her a great honor in January. He

106

had appointed her his Court Singer. At nineteen, she had gone as far as it was possible to go. In Stockholm at least. But could she be satisfied with the standards here? She shook her head, and the reflection in the mirror shook its head, too.

She laid down the brush and sighed. "I must leave Sweden if I am to gain perfection! I must save, and some day go to Paris to learn more from Manuel Garcia."

CHAPTER X

It was the day of the week when Jenny always had midday dinner with her mother. Her father generally made a point of being there, too, for it was his best chance of seeing his daughter. Fru Lind always cooked a good dinner that day. It seemed as if, by providing special dainties and heaping up Jenny's plate, she sought to remove the memory of the hard words she had spoken.

But they got on better together now they were not under the same roof. The meal was an amicable, almost a happy one. Afterward they had coffee in great elegance, in the little parlor where Jenny used to sleep. The bed had been removed, and the piano lid opened to show that there was no objection to a little music. The room was fragrant with the bouquets from the final performance of the season. Jenny had given them to her mother.

"So now," said Fru Lind, "I suppose you will be planning a holiday in the country? Lucky girl!"

"Not entirely a holiday," Jenny answered. "I have to give several concerts and end up with singing in Gothenburg before I am free."

"A wonderful port, Gothenburg," her father remarked, "fine cafés and taverns and—er—buildings of every sort."

Her mother sighed. "And on the sea, too! What would I not give for a breath of the open sea!"

Jenny darted a somewhat frightened look at her. Was this a hint? She knew the concert would be a failure if her mother accompanied her there. Fru Lind would become difficult again, would insist on the concert tickets being raised in price, and become offended if she was not offered the best seat in the hall.

"Don't forget, Gothenburg is a port, a large town, Mama," she told her. "And you know you always like to go to a quiet place."

Fortunately it was true. Her mother nodded her head. "Yes, give me the peace of the country. All the same, Jenny, I don't like you traveling about alone. For a young woman, it is not correct."

Jenny glanced across at her father. She saw a gleam in his eye.

Afterward he escorted her back to the Lindbads'. They crossed the Humlegården, where she and Amalia had played years ago. Already the trees had put out their leaves. Smart women bowled by in their carriages, lured out in the soft spring sunshine like butterflies.

Niclas Lind followed them appreciatively with his eyes. Jenny had to speak twice before he paid her any attention. "Papa," she was saying, "would you like to travel with me to Gothenburg? The Lindbads can't come."

"To escort you to Gothenburg? Certainly, my dear. With pleasure."

"I think Mama means it when she says she prefers the country. I've always noticed she is quieter and calmer after a country holiday."

"Yes, that's true. Her nerves need soothing. Yes, indeed, she should certainly go to the country."

Something in the heartiness of his reply, made Jenny feel mischievous. "The country would suit you *both*. There are no temptations there, are there? Let me tell you a secret, Papa. I'm saving hard at present. There's—something—I want to do for myself. But I always promised to buy a little house in the country for you, and I'll keep that promise first."

"*Me* live in the country?" His jaw dropped.

"Yes," she said firmly. "It would break you from your bad companions and do you all the good in the world. Wouldn't it?"

"I suppose so." But his voice of dismay was so comical, she nearly laughed.

Then she said persuasively, "You know you would get to like it. I would buy you a nice little house, with a garden. You said you always wanted to grow vegetables. And a lake or some water near by, where you could fish. It really wouldn't be so bad!"

He began to think of catching large fish and grew happier. There was bound to be an inn somewhere, where he could boast of his catch of an evening. "You promise there will be good fishing?"

"I promise, faithfully. And—you know, Mama will be much more sweet-tempered when she doesn't have to see me so often. I dare say you will be happier together than you have been for a long while."

"Jenny!"

She turned her large gray eyes on him. They were full of pain now. "She never wanted me, you see. She loved Amalia, but not me. I was only a burden to her. That was what was at the root of the matter."

"Jenny dear!" He tucked her arm more firmly under his and they walked the rest of the way in silence.

It was warm summer weather by the time they set out for Gothenburg. Jenny sat entranced by the landscape seen through the carriage windows. Great forests swam into view and then withdrew to allow glimpses of fields and blue water. Always lakes, big or little, fringed by the silver birches she remembered dimly around the lake of Sollentuna. Sometimes a noble castle reared its head above the woods or mirrored itself in the water. This part of Sweden was the favorite hunting district of the Swedish nobles, and many of them had their summer homes here.

Gothenburg was a different matter. It was busy with trade and importance. Timber was exported from it all over the world. At night, in their hotel, they could hear the boat signals coming from the harbor, and by day, the hammer-hammer from the shipyards. The whole town was plastered with notices when they arrived. GRAND CONCERT! MADAME JENNY LIND! FRESH FROM HER STOCKHOLM TRIUMPHS! Niclas Lind delivered Jenny to their hotel and then strolled through Gothenburg, reading the notices with pleasure. But the one he liked best was on the doors of the Concert Hall itself. It said briefly: SOLD OUT.

Gothenburg was full of people from the country who had taken this opportunity of hearing the famous Nightingale. The hotels were packed. Jenny had her own sitting room, so could avoid the stares of the other guests.

111

Only after the concert itself did she consent to drive a little along the coast for a breath of fresh air before going to bed.

There was still some light in the sky. The sea had turned a strange color, and against it, a ship showed black, flying the Danish flag. Lind looked at it wistfully. "That's the packet boat going over to Copenhagen. I've never been there."

Jenny was feeling grateful to her father for his kindly care of her. She did not like cities, and she did not particularly care about a sea passage. But here they were, and with some time on hand before she was due on a country-house visit.

"Would you like us to go there, Papa?"

"Of course, of course! You always humor your old papa, don't you, my dear?"

Jenny squeezed his arm affectionately. She was pleased by his pleasure. And besides, after all, perhaps it was time that she saw a little more of the world. They could make it part of the holiday, too. She knew no one in Copenhagen, so would not be required to sing, or make a display of herself. Lind was a common name. Herr Lind and his daughter could stay in some modest hotel —not the sort of hotel in which anyone would expect to find a prima donna—and even the newspapers wouldn't know. . . .

A few days later they sailed into Copenhagen harbor. The wide stretch of water seemed almost to engulf the city before them. It was far vaster than Stockholm Harbor, and crammed with many more ships. Niclas stared eagerly at the huge four-masted barque from Finland, and the British man-o-war lying farther out. It was evening now, and the light had failed faster than it did farther north. The lighthouse of Elsinore winked through the dusk. The ramparts and pleasure gardens surrounding the crescent bay were shrouded in dusk.

Unlike most harbors, the ships could sail here right up to the quays. They disembarked and took a cab to one of the smaller hotels in the city. Here, as planned by Jenny, her father merely registered as "Herr Lind and Daughter, from Stockholm." It was a pleasure to be greeted as ordinary travelers; not to be stared at; to climb the stairs to their rooms without crowds trying to catch a glimpse of The Nightingale. But indeed nobody would think of looking twice at the pale, dowdy young woman who climbed them. Though some of the women looked again at the handsome man who accompanied her.

A chambermaid brought hot water and clean towels to Jenny's room. Like most Copenhageners, she was much more talkative and friendly than the stiffer Swedes. "The lady looks tired!" she said sympathetically, draping a towel over the ewer to keep the water hot. "I can bring supper up to the room if you prefer to go to bed early. Then you will be fresh for tomorrow."

Jenny unfastened her bonnet strings. "What happens tomorrow?"

The girl looked at her, astonished. "Why, tomorrow is Constitution Day! Did the lady not know? It is our great fête day. All sorts of things are happening tomorrow! A public holiday, and a gala performance at the theater. And the golden apples will rise in Gammeltorv Fountain!"

113

Golden apples. As Jenny was falling asleep that night, she smiled and felt happy at coming here after all. This must be a fairy city. Father will enjoy himself, and perhaps, in spite of not liking cities, I shall enjoy myself too. . . .

Next day the flags were out and bands playing. Jenny and her father strolled out along the Bredgade, past the enormous ruin of the Marble Church, and paused before the four little palaces which make up the royal town residence of Amalienborg. The sea must run past the end of the royal street, too; for as they stood, they saw masts glide mysteriously past in the distance.

"Nice for the King to watch his ships from his own front windows," Niclas remarked. Then his attention was attracted to the changing of the guard. The soldiers looked as if they were wearing toy uniforms, they were so brightly clad. And they paced stiffly like toys, so that one could scarcely take them for soldiers at all.

"I like this Copenhagen," Niclas said. "It is a light-hearted place."

"Now we must see the golden apples," said Jenny.

But Niclas was thinking of his lunch. "Let us eat first."

They had a fish dinner in one of the restaurants down by the quays. Jenny sighed with happiness. Here, at last, she could do what she liked, eat where she wished, with no comments or staring!

"Promise, Papa, you will tell nobody who I am!" she begged him urgently over the table.

"Have I not already promised that?" he countered reproachfully.

114

She flashed at him one on the charming smiles which transformed her face. "You like to boast about me, I know. So you might be tempted to break your promise!"

"It's true I am a proud papa. A *very* proud papa. But my Jenny's comfort comes first. So I will promise again. Here, in this glass of schnapps!" And he raised his glass solemnly toward her.

They rose and walked slowly back into the town. Now they were crossing the Kongens Nytorv, the main Square, ringed about by fashionable hotels and restaurants and dominated by the enormous hulk of the Royal Theater. As they brushed by one of the posters, Niclas stopped and read it. It announced a gala performance, that evening, before the King and Queen of Denmark.

But the *clou* of the announcement was, that Madame Heiberg was performing that night.

Niclas said irresolutely, "My Jenny wants peace, and a rest from all theaters. And yet—I have never seen The Heiberg perform. By all accounts she sounds extraordinary."

Jenny opened her lips to tell him to go by himself, she would stay alone in the hotel. Then it flashed across her mind that her papa would scarcely come home tamely at a reasonable hour if he went there alone. Likely enough he would pick up some raffish acquaintance and spend the rest of the night in one or other of the surrounding wineshops.

Besides, she felt some curiosity, herself, about the acting of the famous Madame Heiberg. It was well known, even as far away as Sweden, that Copenhagen was crazy about her. She was said to be by far the finest actress Denmark had ever produced. Everything from bonnets and shawls to spades and shovels, was called Heiberg in compliment to her. They said she could entrance an audience, hold it spellbound, just as Jenny herself did, in Stockholm, across the Sound.

Jenny felt humble that so great a genius was bound to teach her something about acting, just as Garcia could about singing. After all, the Danes had had a longer tradition of first-rate theater than was to be found in the other northern capitals.

"Let us both go and see The Heiberg tonight," she told her father. "Will you get two tickets while I wait here?"

His face beamed with pleasure. Her own heart warmed to see how, after all, her beloved papa would rather be with his daughter than with anyone else. He disappeared up the steps toward the box office while she stood near the bottom, watching the crowds that passed and repassed the Square.

It was a long while before he returned. When he did, he waved two bits of pasteboard triumphantly. "We're lucky! All the seats were sold out long ago, but——"

"Papa!" she cried reproachfully. "You *promised* not to mention my name!"

"I didn't. But, well when they told me that and brushed me aside, I nearly forgot my promise. I nearly told them by whom the tickets were required. That would have instantly produced a box for my Jenny!"

"But—you didn't, and yet you got the tickets?"

Seeing the panic in her face, he decided he had teased her enough. "A gentleman stood before me at the ticket

116

office. He was returning two tickets because his wife was ill. You can be sure I bought them on the spot!"

She was so relieved, she kissed him there, on the street. Then, after inquiring the way, they turned off Kongens Nytorv into a long, narrow street lined with fine shops. Presently this street widened into another, smaller square. And here stood the Gammeltorv Fountain. But they could scarcely see it at first, for the mob of children surrounding it.

They edged their way through the children until they stood close to the Fountain. Its waters ran into a large basin, and there, in the basin, were the golden apples, bobbing around and sometimes shooting high in the air with the pressure of the water about them.

"Pretty!" Jenny laughed, clapping her hands.

"Pretty! Oh pretty!" A child's voice echoed, beside her.

"Charlotte! Don't go so near. You will tumble in——"

The voice of the man speaking to the child arrested her attention. She turned around sharply to see who it was, and recognized, in the dapper figure clutching a child in each hand, the visitor to her dressing room the winter before. August Bournonville himself.

117

"Mademoiselle Jenny Lind!" His pleasure was obvious. He turned hastily to the child. "Charlotte! curtsey to the lady. This the famous——"

"Oh please! Please!" Jenny put up her hand in horror. Already several people in the crowd were looking at her, though she hoped and prayed they had not heard her name. "I'm here incognito," she added, lowering her voice, "I didn't want anyone to know——"

"Who you are? Forgive me then. And let us step back a little to talk. But you must at least allow me to present my wife. She is over there on the pavement. She said she had seen the golden apples often enough."

Jenny and her father made their way through the seething mass of children and parents. Short of rudeness there was nothing else to do. But when she saw the gentle figure standing in the shelter of a shop entrance, she liked the look of her at once. And she liked her still more when Madame Bournonville spoke to her in Swedish, which was the native tongue of them both.

"I am always so proud of you, Mademoiselle Lind! When I think that my own country has produced——"

Her husband, who had had only time to pronounce Jenny's name now intervened hastily. "She wishes to be unknown. We must not embarrass her, my dear."

Jenny glanced at him gratefully. She introduced her father, and they strolled along the pavement together, much to the disappointment of the little Charlotte, who had wanted to see the golden apples again. But Jenny was terrified someone in the crowd might have overheard her name, and the Bournonvilles tactfully recognized her wish to remove herself as quickly as possible.

The little boy trotted along beside her, dressed in his Sunday best; white trousers and a blue jacket with shining brass buttons. He looked up at her face now and then, and presently asked, "Do you like my new jacket?"

"Let me examine the buttons," Jenny stopped and bent down to look at them.

"And my new dress! This is my best new dress!" Charlotte caught hold of her other hand, then turned around proudly to display her sash.

"Don't let these imps bother you," their father exclaimed. But Jenny only smiled and walked on, holding each child now by the hand. "I love children. And I think they generally take to me."

It was true. Her shyness always vanished when there were children about. She talked of their interests gravely, as if such things were as important to her as to them. The Bournonvilles looked pleased. When they parted at the corner of the street, Madame Bournonville asked what hotel they were staying at.

"I understand and respect your wish for privacy. But while you and your father are here in Copenhagen, won't you give us the pleasure of your company at supper some evening? I promise you won't be asked to sing!"

Now that Jenny had met such an agreeable family, now that she had made the acquaintance of the two charming children, she accepted at once. An evening was fixed, and Monsieur Bournonville gave them one of his cards.

"We live in an old-fashioned house in an old-fashioned part of the city. But perhaps you won't object to that!"

Certainly the Linds did not. It was pleasant, after all, to have acquaintances in a strange place, especially when the head of the family was an artist like herself and understood the artist's need of occasional quiet and withdrawal. After this meeting, there was just time to return to the hotel and dress for the theater. And Jenny set out with her father, amused at the thought of sitting on the wrong side of the footlights for once.

The lines of carriages deposited their occupants before the Royal Theater, then drove away again. Comparative silence fell, though the café lights blazed and the restaurants were full of disgruntled diners unable to get seats for the great performance. Inside the theater nobody paid any attention to the simply dressed girl of nineteen sitting beside her father. They had no attention to spare, anyway, for anyone except the great actress they had come to see.

Jenny re-entered their hotel again, still and dazed. The coffee room was deserted. They sat down at a table, and Lind, observing her rather nervously, said, "Well, my dear?"

"Papa," Jenny said slowly, "that was the perfection of acting. I could never hope to imitate her success!"

"Nonsense!" her father said stoutly, "there was no heart in the performance. Not such as you put in yours!"

"Then why were you wiping your eyes in the last

scene? I have never seen you weep in a theater before."

"A touch of cold. I believe I got it on deck last night."

"Don't deceive either of us, Papa. That was *great* acting. I move people because I am natural, I feel my parts so they feel with me. And I have my voice. But *that*—what we have seen and heard tonight—was genius."

"And have you not genius too, Jenny?" her father said softly.

"Perhaps God gave it to me, too. But he gave it to me through my voice. And she has beauty. That I have not. I think she is the most beautiful woman I have seen in my life."

Her father was silent. He was thinking so, too. And he was a connoisseur of female beauty. Jenny, too, was thinking. She was remembering what Bournonville had hinted at, last winter.

"And the applause," she said. "The people are mad about her. They adore her. They adore her beauty. Never, never, could I perform in Copenhagen in competition with her!"

A few nights after this, they visited the Bournonvilles for supper. In the amber light of a still evening they entered Nikolaj Plads and sought out the house. This little quiet square lies behind a busier street and is dominated by the old church in the middle. One buttress-support of the church springs right over the path so that they had to step beneath it to reach the end of the square.

The Bournonvilles' house was at a corner. You had to descend two steps to reach the front door, which was heavily carved in the ancient manner. Already Copen-

121

hageners considered this quarter too old-fashioned to live in, but August liked its quietude, and the roominess of the house.

A servant took them into the vestibule and led them up the narrow stairway to the drawing room above. Madame Bournonville received them with simple kindness which warmed Jenny's heart. The piano in a corner of the room had been closed, Jenny noticed. She was grateful for this sign of tact.

"Miss Lind! Please let me kiss you before I go to bed!" Charlotte had sprung up from a window seat and threw herself into Jenny's arms. Jenny gave her a hug, then relinquished her as her mother said, "That will do, Charlotte. Now you have given your greeting, off you go!"

The pretty child waved from the door. "You will come and say good night to us after supper?"

Jenny nodded and Charlotte scampered away. Presently the grownups went downstairs again where a light supper was laid out on the dining-room table. There was no fuss; no pretension. But Madame Bournonville had prepared one or two Swedish dishes out of compliment to the visitors. Afterward, in the drawing room once more, they sat by the window to catch the rays of the setting sun which shone greenish through the trees of the square.

Presently Jenny remembered. "The children! May I visit them? I promised——"

"But of course. Charlotte at any rate will be waiting for you. The smaller ones may be asleep."

But they were not. As she opened the drawing room

door, Jenny caught sight of the little boy hanging over the banisters in his nightshirt. "Please come up! We've waited and waited!"

She followed him up the staircase and disappeared. Because it was a warm evening, the drawing room door was left open. Presently there floated down to them— Jenny's voice. She was singing to the little Bournonvilles; singing the Swedish songs their mother sometimes sang to them. But this pure voice transcended anything the listeners had heard before. It was like a nightingale singing in the dusk.

Madame Bournonville wiped her eyes as she listened. "It brings back my own childhood!"

Her husband glanced at Niclas Lind and said with emphasis, "That voice *must* be heard here—in Copenhagen."

Niclas shook his head. "She won't sing here. She's frightened of competing with The Heiberg."

"But The Heiberg is an actress, not a singer!"

"The public has only room in its heart for one at a time, so she believes. Stockholm has taken Jenny to its heart. She thinks Copenhagen lies too much under the spell of The Heiberg to listen to anyone else——"

He broke off as Jenny re-entered the room. She was feeling happy; warmed and at ease. She went straight over to the piano and opened its lid. "I have sung to the children. Would you like me to sing to you?"

The evening darkened, but still they sat in the room without lighting the candles. Jenny was transporting them into a magic land where no candles were necessary. The window was still open, and one or two people, lingering in the square for a breath of coolness, began to gather under it, until August, afraid lest his visitor notice the little crowd when she rose from the piano, closed it decisively.

The strollers beneath raised expectant faces up to the house a minute or two longer. Then, deciding their ears had deceived them, moved on.

That was the first of several pleasant visits to the old house in Nikolaj Plads. August Bournonville kept his promise. No strangers were asked to meet Jenny, and so this pleasant acquaintanceship ripened to friendship. The ballet season was over, and August had time to show his new friends the environs of the city.

Once he and his wife drove them out to the Deer Park, where the great beech trees spread for miles. Another evening they walked on the ramparts surrounding Copenhagen, where burghers and their families loved to stroll when the air got cool. The earthworks that had once protected Copenhagen in times of invasion, were now overgrown with grass and made a pleasant promenade. Where the open country stretched before them, a windmill still tossed its arms in the air. Behind the old ramparts, the city spires went up to meet the sky and the evening bells rang from them, over the harbor toward Sweden.

August Bournonville being a famous figure met many acquaintances, but if Jenny was on his arm he merely raised his hat and did not stop to introduce anyone to her. She was grateful for that, too. But often she would attempt to slip away from him to her father's side, saying, "Greet your friends! Don't let me keep you from them!"

Most of his friends looked gay and fashionable. Once, however, looking back, she saw him in earnest conversation with a shabby figure so odd in its appearance, she meant to ask who it was, but forgot. It seemed to her that the man looked after her earnestly, and she hoped that August had not forgotten his promise.

Now came the last evening of their visit to Copenhagen. Their passages back to Sweden had been booked for tomorrow's mail packet. The Bournonvilles escorted them to their hotel and lingered a moment, saying goodby.

"Dear Jenny!" Madame Bournonville kissed her affectionately. "You will pay us a visit next year? Please promise!"

"Now I have friends, I will come back gladly." Jenny returned the kiss with warmth.

August Bournonville pressed her hand. "And perhaps —someday you will consent to let Copenhagen hear that wonderful voice?"

She shook her head, smiling a little. "I told you. I shall never compete with The Heiberg. You have your wonderful Star. What light I have would be dimmed completely by her!"

She went upstairs and began to pack. They had walked farther than usual, and she was tired. Tired, too, by the thought of returning to endless rehearsals for Stockholm's forthcoming winter season. The worst of a holiday is, it makes you disinclined to go back to work.

Then she rebuked herself sharply. Don't be lazy, Jenny! You know your work is your life as well.

The chambermaid knocked at her door. It was the same cheerful girl who had waited on her when she arrived. "Beg pardon, but there's a gentleman downstairs, asking to see you."

A gentleman! Perhaps it was August Bournonville returned with some further last message. For she knew no other gentleman here. . . .

She had already slipped off her dress, but put it on again and went downstairs reluctantly. She was very weary and wanted to go to bed. The coffee room was deserted, except for a tall, shambling figure that rose to its feet eagerly as she came in.

She thought, as she looked at him, that she had never in her life seen so ugly a man as this. Why, he's even uglier than me! she decided, surprised. He had an enormous nose, a gash of a mouth, and huge hands, in one of which was clutched a wilting bouquet of flowers.

"Mademoiselle Lind? Permit me to kiss your feet!"

She stared at him; at his eccentric looks, at the wild way he spoke. Then she answered him angrily. "Who gave you my name, Monsieur?"

"My friend August Bournonville. He pointed you out to me. He said you were leaving tomorrow and wished to remain incognito. But one artist must, *must* pay homage to another. I brought you this trifle—those few flowers——"

August Bournonville had done this! For once, in her tiredness she forgot to be gracious. She brushed the flowers angrily away.

"I have not the least idea who you are, but——"

"Pardon me if I forgot to introduce myself. My name is Hans Christian Andersen. I am——"

"I have no interest in your name. I have never heard of you before. I distinctly told Monsieur Bournonville that I desired to make no acquaintances during my visit here. I regret that I cannot receive you. Especially at this extraordinary time of night."

He said, "Once more, I beg your pardon, for my intrusion," and bowed with a queer sort of dignity. Then he turned and walked out of the room, his bouquet, which had cost him such thought and money he could ill spare, still in his hand.

There was something in the droop of his shoulders which made her regret her words as soon as she had spoken. She took a step to recall him. But he was already out of the room. She stood there a few minutes, feeling unhappy. But when her father came in a moment or two afterward, she had recovered her equanimity.

"The hall porter told me you had a visitor. Who was that, my dear?"

"An extraordinary person called Andersen. Papa, it was extremely impertinent of him to call, was it not?"

"Of course, my love. Of course. You are looking exhausted. Come upstairs to your room."

But she still wondered, for a few minutes longer, if she had been needlessly unkind. By the time she had finished her packing, however, she had forgotten even his name. She had no idea that the world would remember that name long after the name of even The Heiberg was forgotten.

CHAPTER XII

It was autumn of the same year, 1840.

The evening air had a nip in it now. Darkness began to come down instead of the long half-dusk. And people lying in bed could hear the wild geese honking over the housetops, could hear even the steady beating of their wings as they passed overhead. Winter is coming, they said, as they turned over to sleep. Soon the Northern Dancers will show themselves in the sky.

In the country, the fields were reaped. The brown stubble stretched to the horizon, and the birches were shedding their leaves. The whole landscape had changed from green to amber. Red-brown in the fields, yellow on the trees and a misty haze over the midday sun; while the fruit in the village gardens had turned yellow, too, and was ripe enough to drop into one's hand.

A Stockholm carriage pulled up before the inn at Sollentuna. Jenny Lind got out and looked about her. The place had not changed, and yet she scarcely remembered it. The innkeeper came out and took her order. The horses to be put up, the coachman given a meal. He had had orders not to mention her name, but nobody asked it. The innkeeper was mildly surprised that any lady so young, so plainly dressed, could have afforded a carriage at all, and driven in it alone.

"The house for sale? Over there——" He pointed toward a neat cottage with a little garden in front. Its windows were shuttered and it was empty. But the advertisement in the Stockholm paper mentioned that the key could be had at the pastor's house. She remembered now, where that was. It stood by the church, and there was the bell tower of the church still standing, blanched by whitewash, against the sky.

She remembered, now, the worn steps of the church, and the day she was pushed out of the building and made to sit on them because the soprano didn't want her inside. She knocked on the door of the Pastor's house and said what she wanted. He was a stranger, too. He fetched the key, delighted.

"The family have left already," he told her, adding, "It is a good house I assure you. The fence was painted only this year."

Then he looked at her curiously. "Are you thinking of residing here among us?"

She shook her head. "It is for my parents. They wish a little house in the country."

She unlocked the door of the empty house and walked through the small rooms, opening each shutter so as to see them properly. The stove in the living room looked a good one, and the accommodation was just what her mother wanted. As for her father, he would be delighted to live on the main road, straight opposite the inn. There was an orchard behind, and a spot of garden in front. Yes, she would buy the house.

She locked the door carefully behind her and left the key back at the parsonage. As she did so, she asked timidly, "There was a family—Ferndal—who lived here once. Fru Ferndal is dead, I know. But her husband?"

"The old sacristan? He died a couple of years ago. Before my time. I have only been Pastor here for a year." Again that curious, inquiring look. "The lady knew them? She has been here before?"

"Not for many, many years." Young as she was, Jenny felt old as she spoke the words. Sixteen years was a long time, after all. . . .

The dinner she had ordered at the inn would scarcely be ready yet. She began to walk through the village, toward the fields. Insensibly, her feet took her across them by the short cut toward the lake. Now she saw the water before her, glittering like a mirror. Papa would find plenty of fish there, surely!

The brown stubble cracked under foot. She remembered the trees fringing the lake, and how they grew taller and taller as she approached them. Suddenly she began to hum under her breath the old, forgotten song, *Where the birch tree bends to the water*. There had been a morning, long ago, when she had come here with Selma, and a woman had been washing clothes and singing.

Jenny stopped suddenly, staring. There *was* a woman down there, washing clothes in the lake. She had a shirt laid out on a big flint stone and was pounding the stuff with the smaller stone she held in her hand. It was exactly the picture that had leaped into Jenny's mind. It made her feel unreal; like somebody in a dream. Perhaps it *was* a dream. Perhaps, in sleep, she had gone back to her childhood, had remembered these things long forgotten, and would presently awake in her own room in the Linbads' house. . . .

But the little house was no dream. She had felt the key lying cold in her hand.

She walked up to the young woman and spoke to her. She looked about the same age as herself. A year or two older, perhaps. "Does the lake water still wash clothes as white as ever?" she asked.

The other girl nodded and stared. Strangers were unusual in Sollentuna. "My mistress is very particular," she said, pausing, with the stone like a sponge in her hand.

"Is she the Pastor's wife?"

"Why no. I work for that farm over there."

Jenny asked suddenly, "What is your name?"

"Selma Norström."

"Selma! Don't you remember me? I'm Jenny Lind!"

The young woman dropped the stone with a crash. "Jenny Lind! Little Jenny, grown so famous away there in Stockholm! We read about you in the papers. When I tell them I used to play with you, they will scarcely believe me!"

Jenny sat down by the lakeside and pulled Selma down beside her. She could scarcely contain her joy at finding a part of her childhood still here in Sollentuna. "Don't tell anyone who I am! Don't think of me as the singer you read about. Think of me as the Ferndals' girl. I loved Fru Ferndal, Selma. She was my only real mother."

"She died years ago. Is that why you never came back?"

"Yes. Tell me about yourself. Do you like working up at the farm?"

Selma shook her head. "My mistress has a bad temper. But there are few places about here, and one mustn't grumble. Sometimes I think of going away and getting work somewhere else. My own mother is dead, did you know that?"

"She kept the best hens in the village. I remember how she would let me watch the chickens breaking out of the egg. . . . Selma dear, you and I are alone in the world. Oh, I know my own mother is living; I'm just going to buy a little house for her here. But I must go out into the world too, to earn my living. Someday, perhaps you will come with me?"

"To Stockholm!" Selma's eyes opened wide.

Jenny said hastily, "Not for a while. Not for a long time, maybe. I must save yet, to pay for the little house, and for—something else. But I work so hard, I have no time to keep my clothes mended, and I am often weary packing and unpacking. Someday—will you come and look after me, Selma?"

"Yes, indeed I will, Jenny!"

It was midday now. The bell from the white tower began to toll slowly. The notes floated over the landscape as far as the lake. Jenny kissed Selma, then jumped to her feet. "When the time comes, I'll write to you. Then, if you are still unhappy here, and not thinking of getting married or anything——"

A slow smile came over Selma's face. "You're not thinking of it yourself?"

The ardent, worshiping gaze of Belletti, the handsome Italian, crossed Jenny's mind. But she shook her head. "Marriage is very serious, Selma. One can be swept away you know, and then regret it afterward." She was thinking of her own parents. "Anyway, whether I'm married or not, I know I shall need you someday!"

Back at the inn she ate the simple meal they had prepared for her and then, since the house suited and there was nothing further to keep her in Sollentuna, ordered the carriage to be brought around to take her back to the city. And the warm remembrance of Selma accompanied her all the way home.

That winter season of opera was one of the hardest she had ever sung in. Her star part was Lucia in Donizetti's *Lucia Di Lammermoor*. The story was taken from Sir Walter Scott's famous novel, The Bride of Lammermoor. It was laid in Scotland, and Jenny wore a plaid skirt, a little black velvet jacket and a cap with an eagle's feather in it. But what did it matter what she wore? The story of the lovers who were parted made people weep and rave over her singing and acting. To the massed audiences who crowded to hear her, she was superb, as usual.

But Jenny herself knew a difference. There was that hoarseness. It showed itself now, toward the end of every performance. No longer could she pretend that she had caught a slight cold; that her voice had been unduly tired by the last performance; that . . .

Anxiously she sprayed her throat, avoided parties with undue talking, refused some of the extra concerts she used to carry through so easily along with her opera commitments. The hoarseness still came. Now she was trying to save her voice, even on the great stage itself. She began her pearly runs lower down. Some of the lovely notes sounded veiled. Still, it seemed that nobody noticed any difference except herself. Perhaps after all, except for the hoarseness, she was wrong?

One day after a rehearsal, the Count knocked on her dressing-room door. He was getting old now, and it was seldom that he troubled to come to the opera at all. A cold shadow fell over her at the sight of him. Had he, by some unusual chance, been present at the rehearsal and noticed she had been singing *mezzo voce* to save her voice for the evening performance?

"Jenny, my dear," he began, "I have a proposal to make to you from the Directors."

"Yes, your Excellency?" Her hands gripped the edge of the dressing table to stop them from trembling.

"It is a new contract. Your old one is running out, you know. Our nightingale has become so famous, we don't want her to fly away. So we propose to gild the cage a little. Let me see——" He raised his single eye-glass to his eye and began to read from a paper he held in his hand.

" 'Wishing most particularly to attach to the Swedish stage a talent so eminent as the Court-Singer, Fröken Jenny Lind, we are making her the highest offer to which our regulations afford us the power.' There, what do you think of that?"

Jenny's hands relaxed their hold. Thank God, she was mistaken about her singing after all! "What is the offer, your Excellency?"

"We are raising your salary to £150 a year. That of itself is far less than your worth, but it is all we are empowered to do. However, you will be given extra service money for every part in which you appear, and also one benefit performance a year. The theater will provide all your costumes. Should you wish to study abroad, you will have the months of July and August free, every summer. Entirely free!"

Jenny looked at him quickly. "Every summer? For how long, then, is the contract to run?"

"For three years. Take it home, child. Sign it at your leisure, and bring it to my office tomorrow morning."

Jenny read the contract through once more when he had gone. She was still reading it, when there came another tap on her door. It was Belletti, wistfully hoping to be allowed to escort her home.

"Belletti!" She was so pleased to see him, she nearly embraced him. "Oh, my dear friend! I've been so worried, so distressed! But now my worries are over. The Directors have offered me a new contract! So what I imagined cannot be so——"

Belletti sat down and looked, not directly at her, but at her reflection in the glass. "What did you imagine?" he asked gently.

"That my voice was—damaged. Oh I can speak frankly to you! You are a singer, too; you and I have sung opposite one another often enough. *I know* that I lack technique still. You with your own fine training have shown me that. But if that is all, I can go to Paris, to Garcia, and learn what they can't teach me here. It was this hoarseness which worried me. Of course nobody notices it but myself——"

She paused, watching him draw a crumpled newspaper from his pocket. "I wondered if I should show you this," he was saying. "Alas! the critics have begun to notice it, too. Read what it says."

It was the report of last night's performance, written by one of the first music critics in Stockholm. She had been working steadily all morning and had had no time to see the papers as yet. The report praised her acting, as usual, but said bluntly that her voice showed signs of fatigue. "Our nightingale failed to sustain her high notes. In some there was even a suspicion of roughness. . . ."

The paper fluttered to the floor. Belletti watched her anxiously, his dark eyes fixed on her face. Presently she said slowly, "That is the first bad notice I have ever received."

"It is not bad, Jenny. It says wonderful things, as usual. But it also tells the truth."

"But the new contract! They would never have offered it unless they were satisfied!"

"Are *you* satisfied?"

There was a long silence. Belletti picked up the contract and read it. "You see? They offer you two summer months of each year to take further training."

"I don't understand. Why should they want to bind me for three whole years in that case?"

"Because they have wind of your project to leave them anyway, to study under Garcia. Once you have reached Paris and your voice is restored, they know very well the whole world will be at your feet. What is the Stockholm Opera, compared with the opera house in Paris? They want to fasten you down, Jenny. That's why they are hurrying you to sign this."

136

She remained thoughtful. Then she said, "Two months under Garcia is not enough. Is it?"

He shook his head. "I am too much your friend to pretend that it is."

She walked home with her hand tucked under his arm. At the Lindbads' door he stopped. "I love you, Jenny. Do you not know what it costs me to say what I'm going to say? Go to Paris. Go now. Get your voice restored by Garcia as soon as possible. I shall not see you while you are there. My own contracts keep me here in Stockholm. It breaks my heart to think how long it may be before I see you again. But go!"

CHAPTER XIII

"Refuse a fine offer like that? You are mad!"

Jenny's mother stopped eating the Christmas goose to stare angrily across the table at her daughter. Jenny had gone out to Sollentuna to spend Christmas with her parents. The little house was decorated with branches of spruce, and the candles were burning brightly on the window sill. Everything had gone well, until she had had to tell them of her determination.

"All the same, Paris is a fine city, so they tell me." Niclas Lind said.

"And how are you going to live in Paris anyway, when you're not earning anything?"

"I've saved enough. I can stay there and study for a year."

"Study what, pray? Are you not the finest singer in Scandinavia already?"

For once Niclas agreed with his wife. Besides, he would miss Jenny badly. "There's no one to touch you. That's right. What's a little hoarseness? Stay with us here for a week or two. The fine air will cure you here!"

Jenny shook her head. "I've made up my mind."

The rest of the evening was gloomy. Even Niclas turned sour at the thought of losing his daughter for a whole year. There were nuts, and a box of sweetmeats, but nobody touched them. Jenny sat, outwardly quiet and composed. She wondered if either of her parents knew how terrified she was at the prospect of leaving Sweden.

"Perhaps I can come and visit you there?" Niclas showed a small gleam of hope. It was quenched directly by Jenny.

"I'm afraid not, Papa. It will take me every penny I have to live there myself. And then there are Garcia's fees. They are very high, I've been told."

She drove away in the darkness next morning. No time even to visit Selma. She was anxious to get back to her friends the Lindbads, to discuss a possibility which had come to her mind during the Christmas dinner.

Adolf Lindbad helped her to make up her mind. He helped her, too, to phrase the difficult letter she must write to the Directors when she sent them back the contract, unsigned. She wrote carefully, painfully, "It is not with half-developed even if happy, natural gifts that an artist can keep his ground; and greatly as I prize the appreciation which I have been fortunate enough already to win, I feel I ought to consider it not so much as a tribute to the artist I was and am, as an encouragement to what I might become."

Then she went on to propose that she should be released in order to spend the whole of the next year, studying under Garcia in Paris. She was willing to accept the contract as it stood, for the two years after that. . . .

Lindbad, looking over her shoulder at this point, said, "But July and August free each summer, is not enough. You should keep yourself free for four months, not two. You need four months, Jenny."

She obediently altered the two months to four. Then she placed her letter, with the amended contract, on the Count's desk on a morning when he was not there, and waited. Presently he summoned her.

"You have driven a hard bargain with us, my dear. But we accept your conditions."

Paris. The nearer it drew, the more she feared and dreaded it. Everyone gave her advice. Her clothes, for instance. "You cannot arrive in Paris looking like that. Don't you know, Jenny, the Parisian women are the best-dressed in the world?"

"My Stockholm dressmaker's good enough for me," Jenny said obstinately. And back she went to the dress-maker who employed Louise Johanson because Louise fitted her so nicely, and besides, she didn't like to take her custom elsewhere.

"You will be asked out very much. You must wear jewels to impress your hostesses!"

"I wear enough tinsel jewels on the stage. Queen Desideria's brooch is all I require."

"The trouble with Jenny is," her father said confidentially to one of his cronies, "she's so darned pigheaded. Always was. Tell her she can't do a thing and she does it at once. Now if we'd all urged her to go to Paris and get lessons from this fellow Garlic or whatever he calls himself, she'd have refused to go."

At last the time came for saying good-bys. Her thoughts turned to Mademoiselle Bayard, now retired and living in a modest part of Stockholm, on her tiny pension. She went out one afternoon to see her, and climbed endless stairs that reminded her of the long

140

stairs up to the flat in Mäster Samuelsgränd.

The old lady opened the door herself. "Why, Jenny!" She was pleased and flattered by the unexpected visit of her star pupil.

"I'm going off to your beloved Paris." Jenny, ushered in to the tiny room, sat down by the stove. "Have you any message you want me to take?"

"Only to Paris herself. The Queen of Cities! My friends there are all dead. But give my love to the City. Tell Paris I've never forgotten her!"

That was not quite true. The old lady's memory had become blurred, so that the city she remembered bore not the slightest resemblance to Paris now. Jenny knew this. She allowed her hostess to brew her a cup of coffee and listened patiently to the stories of Paris under King Louis the Martyr; of Marie Antoinette's beauty; of the glories and courtesies of the old régime.

"Never were there such fine manners seen in the world! I am told there is no deportment in Paris today. People did not lounge back in their chairs then, I assure you! (Sit up, Jenny, you're lounging yourself.) Yes, a fine walk and a good carriage counted for something then. I taught you both, my dear. Perhaps old Bayard may still teach them a few lessons through you!"

Jenny sighed. "I wish you had taught me good French as well."

The old lady nodded. "Your French is atrocious," she said bluntly. "That's what comes of all this singing in Italian. Is French not the language of great literature? But fashions are foolish things."

Jenny had brought her old governess two tickets for

141

her farewell performance. She presented them, and the old lady's eyes brightened. "My niece will accompany me. I haven't attended a performance for so long. The stairs are rather trying when one comes home. . . . But *this* performance I shall not miss!"

Nobody else wanted to miss it either. The box office had never experienced such a run. It was to be a farewell concert, rather than an opera, and Jenny was concerned about choosing the programme. It was easy enough to select favorite arias from her greatest successes in opera; but she wanted to end with something simpler; more natural. Something that expressed her own feelings on leaving her country.

Finally Adolph Lindbad said, "I will write you the song myself."

The concert took place in one of Stockholm's old churches. When every seat was taken, people gladly stood in the aisles or leaned their backs against the pillars or squatted four deep on the steps leading up to the pulpit. Perhaps the operatic arias were hardly suitable for such surroundings; and yet the pure voice with its unearthly quality lifted the music onto another plane. Miraculously, there was no huskiness tonight, no faltering over the highest notes.

People who had read of her purpose in leaving Sweden, whispered to one another, "But what does she want to take lessons for?"

Then came her last song, the song of farewell:

"Oh farewell, my heart's desire, farewell each happy hour!

Slowly now before me rise the mists,
Hide in their chilly bosom all
That I have loved—ah, no, now I have nothing left——"

The voice rose, in heartbreaking tones, up to the vaulted roof. The pillars rang with its cry of loneliness. Nothing left! Nothing left! Always Jenny could make her listeners weep. Now, at the end of the song, she was weeping herself.

They gave a party for her that night, but she sat still and silent. Never before had she realized how fiercely, how deeply, she loved her own country. And she was leaving it of her own free will. Now, indeed, there seemed nothing left.

She had withdrawn to a quiet corner where no one could bother her. Presently Belletti came and sat by her, as still and silent as she. She knew what he wanted to say, and wished to stop him, but she couldn't find the right words.

"Jenny, I have asked you before, will you marry me? After you come back from Paris, I mean. I shall be waiting."

"Dear Giovanni, must I say no, again?"

"You will never find a more faithful love than mine."

"I know it. But—you see, I can't love you back. That's the truth."

He sighed deeply. "There's no one else?"

She shook her head. "There's no one else. Perhaps there never will be. How do I know?"

He smiled a little at that and replied quietly and sadly, "Yes, you will fall in love someday. You cannot awake

143

so much love without returning it, too; someday."

Tomorrow was to be her last in Sweden. When tomorrow came, she had one final call of good-by still to make. It was not so much a call as a summons. She had been sent for by her friend the Queen. For the two had become friends now. The merchant's daughter who wore a crown, and the humbly born little girl who had become the idol of Sweden.

Perhaps (Jenny thought to herself), that is the link which unites us. We neither of us were born to the position we hold now.

The Court had moved out of Stockholm for the summer. The Queen had driven back specially to be present at Jenny's last performance, in *Norma*, at the opera house a few weeks ago. Desideria was not at Drottningholm, however. She had confided to Jenny that the great, heavy summer palace oppressed her.

Long ago, when her husband had first come to rule over Sweden, he had built his French wife a little summer pavilion, called Rosendal. It was entirely in the French taste, and in the taste of the period to which she belonged. It echoed the great period of the First Empire, when Desideria's first suitor, Napoleon, brought in the new fashions in furniture as well as in war.

Now Napoleon was dead, and fashions had changed. But, at Rosendal, Desideria could still imagine herself back in France—the France of her youth. Rosendal stood in the middle of the big semi-island of Djurgården. The scenery about it was natural and Swedish. Djurgården formed a charming oasis of parkland and glittering water, near enough to Stockholm to make a pleasant and enjoyable drive on a summer afternoon.

At the entrance nearest to the city stood the old inn, where the poet Bellman used to meet his friends a generation before. But soon the road wound away into space and silence. Jenny hated anything artificial, and it was almost a shock to her to come suddenly into sight of the little sugar-icing pavilion waiting to receive her.

It was two-storyed, with its ground-floor windows reaching almost to the turf beneath them. Glass doors opened to receive her. There were no royal guards outside the pavilion, and she was greeted by the Queen's favorite lady in waiting, who was now a friend of Jenny's too.

"The Queen is so distressed at your leaving us——" The lady in waiting escorted her through the hall as she spoke. She had discarded the uniform black and white of the ladies of the court, and was wearing a dress as simple as Jenny's own. When she opened the door of the little drawing room, Jenny saw that Desideria was also dressed in a plain summer muslin. But, as became a Frenchwoman, it was exquisitely made, and worn with a cluster of rosebuds at her bosom.

"Jenny, my dear!" The Queen kissed her affectionately. She placed her by her side on the sofa with its Empire stripes of white and cherry red. She began to talk eagerly about Paris.

"It is all changed, I know. Yet how I remember the glitter, the excitement of the old times. I was there, in Paris, during the Hundred Days. . . . That was when the Emperor came back from Elba and rallied his troops again. I was Crown Princess of Sweden then. The wife of one of his Marshals who would not come back and fight for him. . . . My position was difficult, *voyez vous*. Yet, Jean-Baptiste had his duty to his own country; to Sweden. He had no right to involve her in war."

Desideria sighed. She must have been torn in two, thought Jenny, watching her sympathetically. Now the Queen was eying her dress. "Remember to write, and tell me the new fashions. Although you are scarcely the person to do that!"

Jenny laughed. She was glad the Queen had stopped regretting the old days, and had returned to one of her chief interests, fashion. "Your Majesty, even if I went to the best dressmaker in Paris, I could never be chic, like you."

Desideria looked pleased. She touched the flowers tucked into her fichu and glanced with childlike pleasure at the reflection of herself in the mirror opposite. "I've worn well, don't you think? Jean-Baptiste—the King—always tells me that. Ah, but not so well as Josephine who supplanted me in Napoleon's heart! Now, she had real elegance, even to the last."

The lady in waiting came in quietly, placed a bowl of grapes on the table before them, and withdrew again. Desideria pushed the bowl across to Jenny, then helped herself, cramming the rich purple fruit into her mouth like a child.

"They are specially imported from France. The Swedish sun is not warm enough to ripen them properly. I will tell you a secret, Jenny. I hate this cold, northern sun! It shines all day in summer, and almost all night, so that I cannot sleep. And in winter, it refuses to rise at all."

146

"Your Majesty was accustomed to the sun of the south of France. For me, I would fear it."

"Chacun a son goût," said the Queen, helping herself to more grapes. "Yes, even in Paris it did not shine so warmly as in Marseilles. Napoleon thought so, too, but then he was a Corsican. I remember well, Jenny, the first time I saw him! His brother Joseph asked permission to bring him to call. The whole family was living in Marseilles then, you know. The Bonapartes were a wild lot, the girls bold and flirtatious, and all as poor as church mice."

It was a strange picture to Jenny. In her childhood she had heard the Emperor still spoken of with fear. Once he had ruled the world; had given thrones to his brothers and sisters. To think of them all as poor, and living in Marseilles in obscurity, was unbelievable. Yet Desideria had known them like that.

"Yes," said the Queen, spitting out a grape-skin delicately into the saucer she held on her lap. "He—Napoleon—was only a shabby young officer then. Thin, sallow, with a lock of hair eternally falling over his brow and badly polished boots! Our house was luxury to him then. . . . So Joseph married my sister Julie. Napoleon always said he would marry *me*, though I was scarcely more than a child. Yet I loved him, but not as I learned to love Jean-Baptiste. After all, I married the better man."

The sunshine came through the slats of the blinds and lay in gold strips on the floor. "Come," said the Queen, rising suddenly, "let us go outside."

She opened another glass door herself and they

stepped out into the little garden. Here the wild grass grew in tufts, refusing to be tamed into a lawn like the lawns of France. There was a green circle of it, facing the pavilion. In the midst of the circle arose a giant porphyry vase. It brimmed over with pansies, a deep purple color. Desideria paused by the vase.

"He wore purple as Emperor. They took his purple from him and banished him to Saint Helena. But a year ago, the King of France ordered his body to be brought back and buried in Paris. That was a kingly action, since in life they were enemies."

She picked some of the pansies and held them out to Jenny. "They will be dead before you reach Paris, I know. But I ask you this favor. Take them and lay them on his tomb when you get there. Take them from his first love, Désirée Cléry."

Jenny took them without a word. Now the Queen was feeling for something pinned to her dress, half-hidden by the cluster of rosebuds. It was a beautiful little watch set in diamonds.

She bent forward and fastened it onto Jenny's own dress. Then she kissed her on both cheeks. "Farewell my child. Don't leave us alone too long. Let my watch tell you when it is time to return to Sweden."

CHAPTER XIV

A late summer evening in Paris, in the year 1841.

Many of the great houses still remained closed, their owners lingering on in their country chateaux until the shooting began. But some of the older residents in particular had refused to undergo the fatigue of moving their households, or preferred Paris at any season. When the sun blazed down on the streets, they took the air in their own gardens enclosed behind high walls. There was enough society left in Paris just now to make up picnic parties in the Bois, or to meet for music and conversation after the sun went down.

The house of Field-Marshal Soult was one of these. Perhaps the greatest of Napoleon's former generals, he had fought for the Emperor at Waterloo, and had been banished in consequence. A few years later the magnanimous King Louis XVIII, now restored to the throne of his ancestors, had pardoned the old Marshal and given him back his honors. After all, had not Soult fought for France, as well as for Napoleon?

Madame Soult liked to give musical parties in the cool of the evening. She enjoyed introducing novelties to her fashionable friends. Novelties are difficult to find in Paris during the hot weather, when the theaters and operas were closed. She felt triumphant at having found one for tonight.

It was now ten o'clock. But such parties do not begin

until late in smart Parisian society, and this was a very smart party indeed. Enough leaders of Society still remained in the city to make it so; and some even thought the special attraction for that evening was worth the journey back from their country estates and a night spent in town.

They were bidden to hear someone called The Swedish Nightingale.

"Désirée introduced her, I believe." The fat, upholstered dowager who spoke, had been of Désirée Cléry's own generation and knew her well. There were times when her friends suspected that she forgot on purpose to give the Queen of Sweden her proper title.

"Désirée? What does she know about singing!" somebody else exclaimed.

"Oh, she was fond of music as a girl. Used to play and sing a little herself."

A supercilious young man paused beside the two dowagers. "The Scandinavians have no voices," he pronounced. "Or if they have, they have no charm, no chic. This newcomer, Lind, or whatever her name is, is riding for a fall. Besides, we have our Grisi."

"She is not appearing professionally I believe. I was told she is here to take lessons from Garcia."

"So that's why the Maestro is here tonight!" The young man glanced across to where a swarthy figure sat, comfortably smoking a cigar. "Well, if she still needs to take lessons from him——"

"Let us be fair. Garcia can always teach a singer something. And the quality of her voice is, I hear, superb."

Now the major-domo was opening the door. He advanced a few steps and announced in a loud voice, "Mademoiselle Jenny Lind!"

The buzz of conversation was instantly stilled. Everyone knew this was the name of the star of the evening; the novelty Madame Soult had bidden them to meet. Everyone's head was turned to the threshold. They saw a plain, trembling girl pass through the doors; a girl with not an atom of chic or aplomb. A girl in a badly cut dress with no jewelry or ornaments at all.

It must be a mistake! Yet Madame Soult had risen to greet her. Concealing her own disappointment as well as she could, she greeted her visitor kindly and led her to a chair beside herself and the old Marshal. The glittering, elegant throng began to chatter again. But those farthest away, said to each other, "Mon Dieu! And she is what Stockholm calls an opera singer!"

Madame Soult herself felt consternation. Why had the girl not dressed properly to begin with? Still, perhaps her voice would atone for everything. The sooner she was led to the piano the better. . . .

Jenny was sensitive. She knew what the glances meant. Always before, when she was bidden to a large party, the company had already been charmed by her presence on the stage. They had heard her voice before; they were ready to be enchanted by it again. Their pleasurable anticipation had given her courage, had warmed her before she began singing at all.

But the scornful amusement of *this* party—hidden though it was behind a mask of fair words and fine compliments—froze her very soul. For the first time, she was facing the most heartless, the most critical audience in the world: an audience of fine ladies and gentlemen who judged first by appearances. She stared, frightened, at the women with powder and paint on their faces, at the men with their elegant, nonchalant manners. She couldn't possibly sing to them! She couldn't reach their hearts, for they had no hearts. . . .

And Madame Soult had risen, was holding out her hand to lead her to the piano.

"Mademoiselle Lind, will you favor us now?"

Mademoiselle Bayard's training in deportment came to her help. She rose and crossed the floor steadily, with the charming, undulating gait she had practiced as a child. The swarthy Spaniard watched her, saying to himself, at least she can walk!

The candles on either side of the piano cast flickering lights on the keys. Jenny sat with head bent for a second or two, while the light conversation stilled. She had planned beforehand what she would sing. An elaborate aria or two, to warm up her voice and please the company of sophisticated opera goers. But now she knew she could not sing these. Her panic had taken away her breath.

She would sing them the songs of Sweden; of her beloved country she wished she had never left. She played a few simple chords, then began to sing, defiantly, an old folk song whose simplicity struck her audience in the face like cold water. She knew it, but did not care. Let them hear something real, something with heart for a change!

But the heart would not come. She sang mechanically, without the feeling needed to transform such songs.

These people would not understand anyway! Before she was halfway through, the buzz of conversation had broken out again. Nobody had ever talked through Jenny's singing before. Her songs were a failure. She knew it.

She rose from the piano at the end of the last one. There was some polite applause, and a suggestion from her hostess that she should give an encore. Jenny shook her head. "If you will forgive me, Madame. I—I have not yet recovered from the sea voyage. I prefer not to sing again."

As soon as she could, she took her leave. Garcia had been introduced to her and she thought desperately, "What must he think of me? I sang badly. Badly! But tomorrow, when I go to him for my audition it will be different. He is a musician. I shall be able to sing for *him!*"

Luckily she did not overhear his comment upon her. Madame Soult made her way to where the great teacher had seated himself once more. She said, with anxiety in her voice, "What is your opinion of the Queen of Sweden's pet protégée?"

He shook his head slowly. "She may do for the simple Swedes. But she has no allure, no commanding presence. I cannot see her performing before a cultivated audience like the ones here."

"But her voice, Monsieur Garcia? That is your province after all!"

Madame Soult spoke the words almost desperately. Paris could be cruel. She had given this party especially to launch a singer whom the Queen of Sweden had lauded to the skies. And the party was a failure. Paris would laugh next day. Poor Madame Soult! It would say. She invited a crow to sing at her party and called it a nightingale!

Manuel Garcia would not again commit himself. "She was shy—nervous. That in itself is a grave default in an opera singer. She gave us no chance to test her full powers. Perhaps tomorrow, when she comes to sing to me, things may be different."

Jenny went back to her simple rooms and cried herself to sleep. The other guests stayed late, and consoled themselves with cards after their disappointment. Madame Soult felt so humiliated by the fiasco, she had a racking headache before the evening was out. Tomorrow she would write to Désirée and tell her what everyone thought.

Tomorrow came. Jenny ate scarcely anything before setting out for Garcia's house. Even the few songs she had sung last evening, had made her hoarse again. But perhaps that was a good thing after all. For Garcia could then tell her what to do to cure it. He could cure everything, people said.

She walked all the way, from the narrow street where she lodged, to the high white house with the green shutters where Garcia received his pupils. Again nervousness made her tremble and feel icy cold as she rang his bell. She controlled herself fiercely. Was this not what she always felt before every performance? It would surely go when she started to sing!

There was a smell of garlic and cooking in the little hall. She even managed to smile to herself, thinking of

Niclas' effort at Garcia's name. He was sitting in a stuffy little parlor, looking fatter and swarthier than ever. She reminded herself he was Spanish, not French. Surely the Spanish were kinder, more sympathetic than the French?

But he greeted her with an air of indifference. It was obvious to her that he had already formed his opinion of her singing the night before. Never mind! She would sing well this morning and remove that impression. . . .

"You prefer playing your own accompaniment, Mademoiselle?"

He seemed reluctant to move from the easy chair he was wedged in, and merely indicated the piano with a wave of his hand. "Let me hear a few scales," he ordered.

She stood where she was, and ran up a scale. The hoarseness was worse, she could hear it there, at the back of her throat. She stopped long before she had reached the upper notes she had once attacked so effortlessly. He said nothing, gave her no praise. Her notes had been veiled, no longer perfectly matching pearls. She knew it.

"Now we must try an aria, to test your full powers. I shall accompany you after all, it will give you a better chance."

He heaved himself out of his chair like a fat cork coming out of a bottle. He seated himself at the piano and let his plump fingers roam with surprising delicacy over the keys. Talking through the notes, he said, " I have been told that one of your chief parts is Lucia. You have often sung in *Lucia di Lammermoor* I believe?"

155

"I know the whole opera by heart, Monsieur. Last year alone, I sang in it thirty-nine times."

"*Bien.* Then sing me *Percho non ho.*"

It was Jenny's great song, which had always called down the most enthusiastic applause. There was no question of her knowing it. She began hesitatingly. Halfway through she faltered, then rose again to attack the high note which she had always hit effortlessly before. Then something happened that had never happened before. Her voice cracked on the note; failed entirely. Now only the piano rippled on before stopping, too.

She stood there dumb in the middle of the floor. It seemed an eternity before Garcia rose and walked toward her. She felt his large hands on her shoulders, pressing her into a chair. She heard, through a mist of horror, his voice saying something to her.

"Sit down, Mademoiselle. It is better, for I must give you a shock."

She waited, dully. His words seemed to come from far away, so that she could neither understand, nor take them in. He spoke them gently, as one breaks bad news to a child.

"Your voice is worn out. Done."

Still she did not understand. Looking up at his great bulk towering over her, she began to explain, impatiently. "I know it is tired. I told you that. I'm beginning not to be able to depend on it, and that's dreadful. Dreadful!"

His voice sounded again; gentle, grave. He was a kindly man in spite of his rough manners, and he knew he was dealing a mortal blow. "I can restore voices when they are only temporarily fatigued. I cannot remake them."

What he was saying began to penetrate. But she could not believe it yet; she *would* not. "Yes, you can restore a voice!" she said wildly. "Why else should I have come to you all the way from Sweden?"

"I see I must speak more plainly still. Mademoiselle, your singing career is finished."

"Finished!" The eyes fixed on him were filled with terror.

"*Attendez!* How many major parts have you sung, since first you began?"

Only a little while ago she had counted them up for fun. Perhaps to impress him, in case he asked that very question. "I've sung all the great rôles four hundred times. Ever since I was fifteen——"

He interrupted her with an exclamation in Spanish. "And still you are but twenty-one! Cruel, cruel to have worked you so hard! A singer needs complete rest between the ages of fifteen and seventeen. They've wound you up like a musical box. And now the springs are broken. Broken completely, I tell you."

She sat quiet, clasping her hands. Impossible to think; to speak, to do anything but listen to his words repeating themselves over and over inside her head. Broken completely. Finished. . . .

The room became suddenly dark. She felt his hand supporting her head while he held a glass of water to her lips. She heard him say, "I am sorry indeed, Mademoiselle. But I had to tell you the truth."

157

The mists cleared suddenly. Her spirit, quenched for the moment, rose to repel this catastrophe. She pushed the glass away, saying, "I cannot believe it. I *won't* believe it. You have heard me when I am tired out by a long season at home; when I have just come through a bad sea voyage. You must let me try again."

"What, now? When your upper register——"

"Not now. In a little while. When I am rested."

He spoke once more as if humoring a child. "It would be useless. Can you not understand? I have come across cases like this before. When a voice has been abused like yours, it never returns."

"Have you ever come across a voice like mine before? Oh I don't speak boastfully, I know it was a gift from God. Surely He doesn't intend to take back that gift!"

He gazed down at her, stroking his long mustache. This one showed a strength of will, a persistence, unique in his experience of the world's singers. And if she were unique in one way, perhaps . . .

At last he said slowly, "You may come back to me in six weeks' time. Meanwhile, you must not sing a note. You must not speak, even, if it can be avoided. But I make no promises; hold out no hopes."

CHAPTER XV

The house in which Jenny boarded, stood in a crooked little street, narrow and dark. Paris had not yet been made wide and splendid, as it was to be later on. It was still the Paris of ancient days, where the sky was scarcely seen for the tall old buildings that crowded close to each other. But the house opposite had gay window boxes, and the flowers in them cheered her a little. That was a good thing, for she stayed in her own little room most of the day.

She was not asked out of it anywhere. She had no friends here. The fiasco of her appearance at Madame Soult's had been enough to stem any desire to invite her to other grand houses. She would not have gone to them in any case. She had sworn to herself not to sing and, if possible, not to speak.

She explained to her landlady, who was sympathetic. Her food was served in her room, so that she need not join the other boarders at meals and be forced to speak to them. For the rest, this glittering, roaring city repelled her too much for her to want to explore it alone.

Sometimes the cries of the street vendors reached her window, behind which she sat in deadly despair. Long afterward, in moments of depression, she could remember their very cadence; could see again the glass-mender trudging past with his panes of glass strapped on his back; hear his wavering cry *"Ah! le vitrier! Ah, le vitrier!*" When the old woman who sold vegetables made her rounds, she recognized her little tune even before the words were intelligible; "*Haricots! Haricots verts!*" And in the early mornings when she lay sleepless, trying to compose a letter in her mind to let her parents and the Lindbads know what had happened to her, the unspoken words would be punctuated by the trit-trot of sharp little hoofs, as the goatherd drove his flock up and down the street, pausing before the doors where jugs were left out to milk one of his herd.

All those little sounds became agony to her. And at last, she was glad when she came upon a faded bunch of flowers among her belongings. The pansies Queen Desideria had given her to put on Napoleon's tomb! How could she have forgotten this commission? She must venture out with them at once. It would be something to do.

Glad, in a way, to be forced outside of herself, she put on her bonnet and ventured into the streets. The Emperor's body had only been brought back from St. Helena the year before. It had been laid, she knew, in a great tomb in Les Invalides, the Home for old soldiers wounded in the wars of France. But how was she to get to Les Invalides from here?

She made one or two timid inquiries. In every case her bad French led to misunderstandings, to smiles and shrugged shoulders. At last she encountered somebody more understanding; somebody who made out her atrocious pronunciation and could direct her. Even as she turned away, after thanking him, she found herself thinking: I must improve my French. How can I sing in a French rôle if nobody understands what I say?

160

Quickly she put out of her mind the probability that she would never sing any rôle again—even in Swedish. She concentrated on the directions she had just been given. And soon this majestic palace of stone with its courtyards, its old soldiers hobbling about, its stained battle flags, stood before her.

She dropped the withered bunch of flowers on the tomb of the man who had ruled the world. As she did so, she thought of him as the Queen's suitor; as the shabby young officer who had overcome everything—poverty, disdain, a humble position, because he believed in what he called his Star.

She too would believe in her Star.

On the way home she passed a stationer's shop. She went in and bought a number of penny notebooks and a French dictionary. After a moment, she also asked for an Italian dictionary as well, and a good French and Italian Grammar. No longer would she stay weakly in her room, doing nothing.

She spent the long days now, studying both languages. It had been all very well, in Sweden, to sing her rôles in her own language. That would no longer do. She worked steadily, filling up the notebooks with lists of vowels, of declensions, of exceptions, of short, stilted essays in French or Italian. When the notebooks were filled, she bought large sheets of foolscap and presently finished them, too. One can still see twenty-three of these filled with exercises in French, and sixty-one in Italian. They were the fruit of her six weeks' "idleness."

At last the day came for her return visit to Garcia. She walked from the humbler quarter where she was living, to the fashionable part where he lived. People were beginning to come back to the capital. The streets were more crowded than ever. The concierge admitted her and she walked up to his second-floor flat. The same smell of garlic in the hall. The same stuffy parlor, its windows sealed in spite of the late summer heat.

"Now, Mademoiselle. Once more a scale."

And the same indifference, though tinged this time, with more kindness. The huskiness seemed to have gone a little from her voice. That was all.

When he had finished the tests he gave her, he leaned back in his chair. "It is as I thought. Your training was wrong from the beginning. They have taught you wrong breathing. Proper breathing is the foundation of every voice."

She was firmer this time. "That at least, you can teach me, Monsieur."

"That I can teach you, of course. But will it bring the voice back? Think carefully. I can guarantee you nothing. And my lessons cost money. Besides, you must live here, in Paris. That will cost you money, too."

She said, "I know. I've saved. I can live here in Paris a year, if necessary."

"It will be necessary. But at the end? If the voice is not restored, you will have spent your savings for nothing. Believe me, I speak in your own interests. You are a good accompanist. Perhaps with that gift, you can still earn your living. Or you can teach singing. But to throw good money away——"

She interrupted him. "It is my money. If I want to throw it away, what does it matter to you, so long as

162

you are paid?"

He stared at her with something like respect showing in his small, dark eyes. "Well then, I will do what you wish. But I must humble your pride first. It is something to ask a prima donna to go back to her very first lessons —and unlearn them. Can you do that?"

"You do not understand me. I have no pride."

He began, somewhat roughly, to test her. He gave her the first simple exercises she had had as a child from Herr Craelius. Ah! Ah! Ah! No trills now; not even scales as yet. And she obeyed him like a child. Breathing the way he showed her.

The Swedish Nightingale had gone back to school.

Now the days passed swiftly for Jenny. Presently he advanced her to scales. Sitting in her little room one night, high up above the street, Jenny wrote to a friend: "I have already had five lessons from Senor Garcia . . . I have to begin again, from the beginning; to sing scales up and down slowly, with great care; then to practise the Shake—awfully slowly; and to try to get rid of the hoarseness if possible. However, he is very particular about breathing. I trust I have made a happy choice. Anyhow, he is the best master; and expensive enough— twenty francs an hour. But what does that signify, if only he can teach me to sing?"

The winter cold came down upon Paris. Jenny found her money was running out alarmingly. She moved from the somewhat humble lodgings she had found at first, to a little room that was even cheaper. Christmas and New Year came. Jenny thought of the Christmas candles blazing at home in her beloved Sweden. She ate her own

163

simple meal alone, with a great loneliness in her heart.

One day Garcia said to her, "The voice is improving. One cannot deny it. But, Mademoiselle, what of your acting? You go nowhere, see nobody. Should you not study our great stars of the stage? Is there nothing to be learned from them?"

So Jenny obediently went to see the great tragedienne, Rachel. Nobody could touch Rachel, she was told. The thin, dynamic young actress held Paris in thrall. Just as on the night she went to see Madame Heiberg in Copenhagen, so, this night, there was the same rustle of anticipation in the audience. The theater itself was a thousand times more splendid than any she had been in before; the audience a thousand times better dressed. Bare shoulders gleamed, opera glasses were leveled; and the orchestra playing in the pit could hardly make itself heard above the buzz of fashionable conversation.

But there was a dead stillness when the curtain went up. Everyone else but Jenny knew what they would see. They saw a thin, plain woman come on the stage and dominate it from the first word she spoke till the last. They felt their own souls shaken by Rachel's emotions; saw life through Rachel's eyes. And they drove home afterward, saying, "We have seen the finest actress in the world, and we possess her here, in Paris!"

Jenny went home in a whirl of emotion, too. Once more in her quiet little room, however, she began to put her thoughts together. She need consider nothing but the actress' ability; there was no beauty to cloud her judgement. Though it was late, she placed her candle on the edge of the table, and sat down to write about the

164

evening to her friends the Lindbads.

"Shall I tell you what I think? The difference between Rachel and me is that she can be splendid when angry—but tender she cannot be. I am desperately ugly, and nasty, too, when I am angry, but am better at being tender, I believe." She bit her pen, reading over what she had written. It looked arrogant, so she added another sentence. "Of course I do not compare myself with Rachel. Heaven preserve us! She is infinitely better than poor me!"

Winter vanished. Spring was in the air now. And, slowly but surely, Jenny's voice was reborn again. The flower sellers reappeared in the streets, and in the public gardens men were bedding out plants. She passed them unheeding on her way to her lessons. They were not real flowers to her, they were reared in hot houses like the ladies who drove by in their carriages. Oh, if she could only have seen once again, the white windflowers under the trees at home!

Besides, Sophie Lindbad had written a letter which frightened her. She had told Jenny she *must* appear in public before returning to Sweden. If she didn't, her public there would consider she had not proved herself good enough for Paris.

She wrote again, a special letter to Sophie. "I dare not tell you how I long for home! . . . To sing without a name is difficult; for here all depends on the accessories. It makes no difference how little talent one has. . . . With regard to my acting, I can compete with anyone here. But there are many other things I lack. . . . For my part, I only want to go home."

CHAPTER XVI

One day in June, Garcia had a visitor.

His housekeeper entered and laid a visiting card on the table beside him. Her master frowned. "Do you not know very well that Mademoiselle Lind arrives for her lesson directly? You should have bade him come back another time."

The woman hesitated. "He said he was a friend of hers."

Garcia picked up the card and read it. It announced Herr Adolf Lindbad, from Stockholm.

"Show him up."

Adolf entered the room anxiously. "Forgive this intrusion! Mademoiselle Lind is an old friend of myself and my wife. I wanted to see you before she came here—to see you alone. How is her voice?"

The Spaniard's eyes lit up. "Superb! It is a miracle. But she has contributed to that herself. Never have I seen such hard work. Such courage!"

Adolf wiped his forehead. "She hinted in her letters that it was restored. But we scarcely dared hope——"

"Listen, thou friend of Jenny! Her range now extends from the B below the stave, two full octaves and a sixth! Never have I experienced anything like it. Her middle voice shows no break, no break whatever. And her shake! Its brilliance, its accuracy is unequaled in my whole experience of teaching. Your country has produced a voice that will astonish the world!"

Adolf Lindbad sank into a chair. He was speechless
with relief. All that winter he and his wife had feared
and hoped for Jenny. She had not dared to tell him all
her own progress. And Garcia had been a hard task-
master, never flattering her, never giving vent to his
own astonished delight at the amazing progress of his
pupil.

Seeing his guest could not answer, the Spaniard went
on. "My tricks of teaching were nothing to her work.
Her practice at home in her lodgings must have been
phenomenal. Never once, never *once*, Monsieur, did I
have to say 'we corrected that mistake last time.' Rather
than oblige me to say that, she would have cut her own
throat!"

"I am inexpressibly happy to hear it, because——"

He broke off at the sound of light steps on the stairs.
Jenny came into the room. She could hardly believe her
eyes. "Adolf! You never told me you were coming to
Paris! My dear, dear friend!"

She hugged him as if he had been her brother. Insensibly she began to speak in Swedish; then corrected
herself with a little smile of apology to her master. The
large hand waved away her excuses.

"I have been telling your friend of your rejuvenation
—of your rebirth. Shall we prove it to him as well? Sing
now, my dear. Let Monsieur Lindbad hear what you
have now become!"

Lindbad listened to her, entranced. All the roulades,
the pearls of ascending scales, the long note held on high
F sharp, held softly, then swelling out and then dying

away without the slightest shrillness or break—he had never heard her sing like this before! And the length of her note was amazing. For she had, more perfectly than any other pupil of Garcia's, learned his great lesson; the lesson of how to replenish her breath while still in full voice, without anyone noticing.

When she finished, she became the old timid Jenny again. "You think I've improved? Even from—from the old days when I sang well at home?"

He took both her hands in his. "Never could I have imagined any improvement, but there is! There is! You sing now more superbly than I have ever heard you."

This was to be one of her final lessons. He sat quietly listening, planning for her, until it was over. But what he had planned, must be cautiously approached. All her letters had said the same thing. She did not want to sing out of her own country, ever. She only wanted to come home. . . .

They said good-by to Garcia and walked out of the house together. Presently she said, "But Adolf, you are not going in the right direction!"

"We are not returning at once to your place. I am taking you to my hotel. There is somebody there who wishes to meet you—to hear you sing."

She looked up at him trustfully. "I will sing now, for any friend of yours. Who is this friend?"

"A very distinguished one I assure you. I told him— but never mind what I told him. It is Giacomo Meyerbeer himself!"

Meyerbeer the famous opera composer! A look of fear replaced the trustful one. "What have you said about me? Have you promised anything? He writes for the great opera houses, for Berlin, for Dresden. Tell me, what have you said?"

"Be calm, Jenny. I promised nothing. How could I, until I heard what your voice was like? He is seeking a soprano to introduce his new opera, *The Prophet*. I only said I might bring you along to sing to him. I left things open in case——"

"In case my voice was not fit for his ears?" He heard with relief the tone of obstinacy in her words. That was the way to manage Jenny! It was just as her father had said. Once hint that a thing is beyond her and she will do it immediately!

Jenny had calmed down again. "But remember, even if he offers me an engagement, I accept none outside of Stockholm. I've learned what it is to be a stranger in a strange land."

He paid no attention to her now. She would sing for Meyerbeer and that, for the moment, was enough. Once she had returned to Sweden and her heart was at rest, she would surely see that no first-rate singer could stay there for the rest of her life?

They entered the hotel and went up to his private sitting room. He had ordered a piano to be placed in it, and there stood the instrument. Before it, picking out tunes idly, was a handsome, dark-haired man. He jumped up and kissed Jenny's hand.

"Our good friend Belletti has many times spoken of your wonderful voice, Mademoiselle. You see, I have come all the way to Paris to hear it."

Jenny dimpled suddenly. "Adolf Lindbad was not so

sure of it, I believe. He told you he *might* bring me here to sing to you. He left the door open for retreat?"

The dark stranger only smiled, then began to play the introduction to one of his own arias. She knew it well. Immediately she took up the air and the room was filled with the pure tones of her voice. Lindbad, listening, wondered again at the transformation Garcia had wrought. Before, she had sung like a bird. Now though the birdlike notes were still there, she sang like the great artist he had made of her.

When she stopped, Meyerbeer's own face was transfigured. "It is the voice I have been longing for, all my life! If you will consent to create my new opera——"

Again her face changed. "Did Adolf not tell you? I am going home, home to Sweden. Your operas always have their first productions in the great opera houses abroad. In Sweden I am safe, I am among my friends. I would never dare challenge the opinion of the world outside it!"

The two men glanced at each other imperceptibly. Meyerbeer's glance said, But this is ridiculous! Adolf's said, Give her time. Leave this to me. Then the composer turned to Jenny saying smoothly, "I understand your feelings, you are homesick, it is natural. But my opera is not finished. You will have plenty of time to reconsider your decision. I beg you to do so."

All the same, as Adolf and Jenny walked back to her house, she said again, decidedly, "It is a wonderful opportunity. I know that. But why should I take it and be unhappy?"

"How do you know you will be unhappy? Have you

not always said your voice is a gift from God, to be spent in the service of man? Have I not heard you say that again and again?"

She hesitated. "Yes, it is true. But can't I serve my own people in my own country?"

He shook his head. "The nightingale sings better when she is flying free through the woods. And you would put yourself in a Swedish cage!"

"Let us not argue," she said gently. "Here is a little garden, artificial and forced like everything in Paris. But at least it has fresh air. Shall we sit down in it for a while?"

He sat down, silent, wondering how he could reopen the subject without offending her. At last he thought of a way. "Your friends the Bournonvilles have been inquiring about you. I saw them last time I was over in Copenhagen."

Innocently, she thought he had dropped the matter. "How is little Charlotte?" she asked eagerly. "And the other children?"

"They are clamoring for you to return to them I believe. And their parents said something of the same sort. Would you not like to visit them again?"

After Paris, Copenhagen seemed quite homelike. "I must take up my contract in autumn, of course. But perhaps—yes, it would be pleasant to sail across the Sound and stay with them for a little. Especially since they don't bother me about singing engagements."

Reluctantly Adolf Lindbad went on. "August Bournonville is anxious for you to appear there as Alice in *Robert le Diable*. It would be a good beginning for you,

171

Jenny. A beginning outside your own country, I mean. That is, if you are frightened at the moment of going farther afield."

"Adolf, you are very persistent! If Monsieur proposes to be equally persistent, I won't go to Copenhagen at all. That's final."

"But Jenny, consider! You would be allowed to sing in Swedish, even though the rest of the cast sing in Danish—the two languages are alike. And it would be a good beginning——"

"Now, don't use that word beginning again! I am beginning nowhere except in Sweden!"

They sat on for a while in the little garden, while Jenny asked eagerly for news of Sophie and all the other friends at home. Adolf was shocked to hear how she had been living in Paris. Seeing no one, going nowhere, except to study the performances of such people as Rachel, Grisi, and Lablache.

"You mustn't shut yourself up in a nunnery!" He told her reproachfully. "This is Paris. Enjoy it. Or as much of it as you can."

She was not made to enjoy a place like Paris. Its fashions meant nothing to her. But with Adolf here, she consented to go to the houses of some of his friends; even to sing for them. And so, presently, a rumor began to spread through the great city. Monsieur Garcia had remade a wonderful voice. Yes, a Swede from the Stockholm Opera House. Famous enough before, it seemed. But what does fame count for if it is only heard in faraway Scandinavia?

Now, people were saying, she could astonish the

world! Naturally, after a year in a city like Paris! These uncouth singers from the north needed polishing up, and she had been polished until she shone surprisingly!

Musicians talked about her more seriously. Meyerbeer talked of that amazing voice after he had left France and gone back to Germany. Even the Germans became curious to hear her. The European world of music is like a great sounding-box. No matter from whence the first echo of a new talent comes, it presently seems to sound everywhere.

In most of the capitals of Europe musicians had begun to discuss one name; Jenny Lind. New talent is always seized upon, to take the place of the old and worn-out. As yet her name was only spoken of among the initiated. It only echoed faintly as yet. Someone had told someone that a girl with an amazing voice like a bird's had been heard at Madame Somebody's party in Paris. . . .

Adolf, before he left, had encouraged her to accept the invitations which came pouring in just as she was about to leave France. Most of them were to sing at private houses, like Madame Soult's. She accepted them because they gave her good training in recovering her poise. Her hard study of the French language gave her ease in conversing with the guests. And she even allowed one kindly Frenchwoman to introduce her to a good dressmaker, so that she could be properly gowned for such occasions. She wore simple enough dresses still, but they were well cut. Paris recognizes a good cut just as quickly as it recognizes talent.

Back home in Stockholm, Adolf Lindbad met August Bournonville who was paying one of his frequent visits there. Bournonville inquired anxiously about Jenny. Was her voice really as good as ever? Because——

"Better than ever. Far, far better than you or I have ever heard it. But I have a disappointment for you, my dear fellow. She'll come and visit you and your wife with pleasure. But, she won't sing in *Robert le Diable*—or anything else."

Bournonville's face fell ludicrously. "I have already promised the Opera Directors that I can persuade her!"

"Then you'll have to unpromise them. She's frightened—scared to death."

"Of The Heiberg? I thought Paris would have cured that nonsense! We'll have her willingly as a guest. I won't even press her to sing if it makes her miserable. But you told her she would be allowed to sing in Swedish? Is there nothing else that would persuade her?"

"You ought to know Jenny by this time. Once she makes up her mind, she won't budge. And if anybody else tries to make up her mind for her, one way or the other, why, that's fatal!"

174

CHAPTER XVII

The sun, that summer of 1843, burned over Sweden all day and half the night.

Jenny's heart lifted with joy at the sight of it once more. The blue lakes, the silver birches, welcomed her home. She could speak her own language now, to everybody. She had returned to the simplicity, the country ways, that she loved.

She spent a few days with her parents at Sollentuna. She praised her mother's new curtains in her little room with its plain wooden walls scrubbed white in her honor. Her father showed her his garden with pride. He had won first prize with his vegetables that summer! She was pleased to notice that he slipped across to the inn less and less, though in fact, the conversation of the country bumpkins bored him, so that now he preferred to fish and garden.

But he asked wistful questions about Paris all the same. "The women, the lovely Parisiennes? Are they as chic as they tell me, Jenny?"

"I don't know." She dimpled at him. "You would have been a better judge of that, Papa!"

"You should have sung in their Opera. You should have been *asked* to sing!" Her mother remarked somewhat angrily.

Jenny shook her head. "I would rather sing in Stockholm Opera House than anywhere else."

"Well, you're going to, I presume, when the season starts. I'm glad to see you have brought back suitable dresses. Suitable, I mean, to your position. You must take care of them properly."

Jenny sighed and the dimples vanished. It was always a burden, looking after one's wardrobe. It took up precious time, too. For she must still practice, if she was not to forget the lessons Garcia taught her.

That evening, strolling across the fields, she met Selma. Struck by a sudden thought, she ran toward her, kissed her and tucked her arm through the other's. "Listen, Selma. I shall have more money now, money to pay for a maid-companion. Do you still want to come to Stockholm with me?"

"To Stockholm!" Selma had scarcely been out of Sollentuna in her life. "Oh Jenny, I'd go anywhere in the world with you!"

"Next winter, then. I have to sing in *Norma* on October the tenth. There are rehearsals, changes of costume, parties even, at which I must sing. Will you meet me there at the beginning of October?"

Selma's face sparkled with joy. "Before that, if you like!"

"No, that will be time enough. I have one or two concerts to give in the south of Sweden, before the end of the summer. And you will be needed here for the harvesting. Besides—I may slip over to Copenhagen in autumn, before the Stockholm season begins."

"Copenhagen?"

Jenny caught the note of regret in her friend's voice. "I've been invited to stay with some friends, the Bournonvilles, there. They have a big family and not much room. I couldn't take you with me this time, Selma."

"Oh well, that's true." Selma sounded resigned now. "And it's true, too, that I shouldn't give up my place at the busiest time of the year. But when autumn comes and the wild geese begin to fly away, I'll fly away too and meet you in Stockholm."

The few large towns in the south of Sweden welcomed Jenny back. They had snatched at the chance of hearing her sing again, before the opera house claimed her once more. Although it was still summer and holiday time, the concert halls were packed as usual when she began her tour. And the critics all wrote that their Jenny's voice was stronger, and more enchanting than ever.

Then she boarded the mail packet and sailed, on a golden day, across the quiet Sound to Denmark. The crossing was so short, she could see the Danish coast opposite her all the way. There were all the white villas dotted along the shore between Copenhagen and Elsinore; and the huge, grim fortress of Kronborg jutting out into the water. The boat glided into the harbor. She disembarked, to find August Bournonville waiting for her, his top hat held respectfully in his hand.

The quiet square with the old church in the middle swallowed her up once more. It was like coming back to a second home. The narrow doorway burst open and the children ran out to welcome her, Charlotte carrying a bouquet of flowers which she dropped in her hurry, then retrieved, dusted, and handed over.

"Darling!" Jenny stooped to kiss them. "It is good to be back!"

After the children had gone to bed, and they were sitting upstairs in the shady drawing room, Bournonville cautiously broached the subject in his mind.

"Your voice is restored. Thank God for that! But now Jenny, for your second lesson—the one even Garcia could not teach you."

"What do you mean?" She looked at him, puzzled.

"I mean, the experience of singing in a foreign city. You *must* gain more confidence. How better could you gain it than by singing here, in a city that understands Swedish and is sympathetic to everything coming from Sweden?"

Jenny made a quick gesture. "Please, don't begin that again! I am flattered, tremendously flattered and grateful that Copenhagen should want to hear me. But I know what will happen if they do."

"What is that?"

"They will start comparing me with The Heiberg. She is their own. They will, in reality, brook no comparison. And I'll lose my confidence again. I have still little enough. The experience of losing my voice still fills me with terror. In Stockholm the people love me. They will give me confidence so that I can sing in opera again. I won't sing anywhere else!"

"But, Jenny, if you don't go out into the world and let the rest of the world hear you——"

She leaned forward, putting her finger on his lips. "Don't you realize that your great people, your geniuses like the dramatist Oehlenschläger, like—like Madame Heiberg—terrify me? This is a far greater city, with far higher standards, than my own little capital. I refuse to

178

face its verdict! I will not do it!"

Because he had to, he remained silent. But that night when undressing, he said to his wife, "What am I to say to the Opera Directors? They relied on me to convey their invitation. She is putting me in a most uncomfortable position! As for The Heiberg——"

"Jenny is not only afraid of The Heiberg. She knows our standards are higher than anywhere else in Scandinavia. She is right about our men of genius. It is they of whom she is really afraid."

He paused, with his neckcloth half unwound. "They all want to meet her anyway. If we could invite, say, one of them here to persuade her!"

His wife considered, then nodded her head slowly. "Of course an unknown genius is a dragon until he is talked to. What about asking Oehlenschläger to dinner?"

He shook his head. "Oehlenschläger is a bit of a rough diamond. Thorwaldsen is in Rome. Besides, he has become a sophisticated man of the world. His social airs would frighten her still more. No, she must meet someone as simple as herself——"

He turned round sharply. "I have it. Hans Christian Andersen!"

Next morning the sun shone high above the golden ball on the top of St. Nicholas Church, casting a green network through the trees onto the cobblestone beneath. Jenny had thought that August would offer to take her for a walk in one of the parks. After all, the ballet school had closed for the season, so he was free.

But apparently he had other plans. "Forgive me if I

179

seem to neglect our distinguished visitor. But I have a call to make. . . ."

Hans Andersen now had a grant from the King, although he was almost as poor as ever. Still he had managed to leave his shabby room in the old quarter, and was now more comfortably ensconced near the Royal Opera House. He had written one or two plays which had had no great success. But the fairy tales which he only wrote to amuse himself and pass an idle hour or two, were now known and loved everywhere in Denmark.

His long, shambling figure was known and loved, too, all over the city. Children followed him in the street, clamoring for a story there and then. Bournonville half-expected to find a cluster of them outside Andersen's lodging. But he only found one little boy who had climbed the stairs and come down again, very disappointed.

"He's out." They both knew who "he" was, so there wasn't any need to say more.

Bournonville, disappointed too, was just turning away, when the little boy ran after him. "But I know where to find him! He goes to the Rosenborg Gardens usually, about this time."

"Come along then. We'll seek him together."

August Bournonville wasn't proud. He thought nothing of walking along the Bredgade in his elegant garb, while a ragged little boy walked by his side. Presently the Gardens came in sight. Brilliant parterres and lawns surrounded the moat which floated around the old Rosenborg Palace. But the little boy headed away from this, toward the wilder part of the Gardens where the beech trees shaded the paths and wild flowers sprinkled the grass.

"He sits here and tells us stories. There he is!"

There he was, leaning forward on a bench, one long bony finger held up for attention. Children surrounded him, listening. Bournonville stepped nearer, to hear the end of the story.

"So they put the soldier in the King's coach, and all three dogs danced in front of it and shouted 'Hurrah!' "

The children shouted Hurrah too, and clapped their hands. The ragged little boy pushed forward, shouting, "What dogs?"

"One with eyes as big as saucers, and another with eyes as big as mill wheels and the third with eyes as big as the Round Tower itself. If you had come in time you would have heard the beginning of the story——" Andersen, catching sight of his friend, pushed two urchins gently off his knees and stood up. "Good morning, August! Do you wish to speak to me about something?"

"Yes, I do. Now you have finished entertaining your friends, perhaps you will stroll with me?"

The children hung about for a little, thinking about the old soldier and the three dogs. Then they ran off. The two men began to saunter down the avenue of trees.

"Andersen," the other began abruptly. "I have come to ask a favor. Will you dine with us tonight?"

The thin, ugly face crinkled into a smile of pleasure. "That's no favor, that is a pleasure for me. Of course I will!"

"We have a guest we want you to meet. A guest from Sweden. Jenny Lind."

The smile vanished. A hurt look took its place. "If you will excuse me, no. Mademoiselle Lind does not like me. I called once, to bring her my compliments. She showed me the door."

"Jenny!" Bournonville looked astonished. "I cannot believe——"

"Oh, it was my fault! You told me she wished to remain incognito. But I felt it my duty to bring her my homage. She didn't want it."

Lord preserve us from two such sensitive beings! August said to himself. Out loud, he said earnestly, "I beg of you to overlook it and come. I'm in a fix, Hans——" And he proceeded to tell his friend about the invitation from the Opera Directors. "She won't hear of it. She's afraid of our talent here. So I thought if she met it in the flesh, met another genius, like yourself——"

"That I might persuade her?" Hans Andersen looked gratified now. "You must not say 'genius' though. Perhaps indeed, my plays——"

August nearly exclaimed, "Tush for your plays!" but he said instead, "You have the power of drawing people to you. Look at these children! Jenny is only a child in her heart. If, in spite of the bad beginning, you can win her and make her believe we are not all ogres here in Copenhagen, I shall be eternally grateful."

The tall, shambling figure paused, drew a pattern in the dust with one shoe, then nodded reluctantly and said, "I will come."

That night, when he was announced, Jenny recog-

182

nized her strange visitor of the time before. But he paid little attention to her at first. He talked to the Bournonville children instead. She could not help listening; could not help being charmed by the way he spoke to them, and their obvious adoration.

Slowly she melted, and so did he. By the time they went down to supper they were old friends. Each had recognized in the other the same sincerity and the same simpleness of mind. After supper Jenny, unasked, went to the piano and enchanted them by her singing. When at last Andersen rose to go, he kissed her hand fervently, and she did not draw back.

"I have heard the Swedish Nightingale and she has inspired me," he told her. "I shall go home now and write a story about another nightingale—who once sang to an Emperor and brought him back from the gates of Death."

August gave him a glance of reminder. Andersen added beseechingly, "Will you not sing for the rest of Copenhagen?"

But Jenny only smiled and shook her head.

For the rest of her visit, Hans Andersen called on her nearly every day. Jenny welcomed him, drew to him, called him her brother. But Andersen wanted more than that. He had fallen deeply in love with his nightingale.

August noticed this; tried to encourage his friend. "Why don't you propose to her?"

Andersen shook his head sadly. "I am poor, and I am hideous. How could I dare?"

CHAPTER XVIII

Now Jenny's visit was drawing to a close. And still August Bournonville could not bring himself to transmit her "No" to the Opera Directors.

He complained to his wife. "They will only think she is proud—or that she wants more money."

"Which isn't true," said Madame Bournonville, placidly darning her son's socks.

"Of course, it isn't. But what am I to say to them? They are drawing up their syllabus now. They want an answer."

"Then you must give them her answer. It is a pity she is so obstinate."

"Yes, I should have remembered that. Lindbad warned me."

"What did he say?"

"He said——" August paused to recollect the exact words. "He said once she makes up her mind, she won't budge. And if anybody else tried to make up her mind for her, that was fatal."

Madame Bournonville dropped her needle suddenly. "August! We used the wrong tactics. Don't you see?"

"See what, my love?" He stared at her animation.

"We have urged her too much! Try the other way. Tell her you see she is right—that it would not do. Then see what happens!"

He embraced her warmly. The mending basket fell to

184

the floor. "My life! You have hit it at last!"

"Calm yourself, dear. And pick up that ball of wool, it has rolled under the sofa." A slow smile dawned on her face. "With all your experience of women, have you not yet learned such a simple fact?"

"Where is she?" he asked eagerly.

"Gone for a walk with the children. I think, to the Amager Torv."

He snatched up his hat and left the house. As he threaded the streets his eye caught fresh posters pasted up. They announced the return of Madame Heiberg in a new play. He reached the little square where the flower-women from the village of Amager sat, wearing newspaper hats to protect them from the sun. He saw Jenny's slight figure standing by the fountain, dabbling one hand in the water.

He touched her on the arm. "I must fetch you home. It is nearly lunchtime."

The children began to run back home, as he had counted upon their doing. He and Jenny walked more slowly. She had bought a few flowers for her hostess. Brilliant-hued asters and even the first chrysanthemums. She looked down at them a little sadly.

"The first signs of autumn! My visit, my beautiful visit, is nearly over. Soon I must begin work again."

This was his opening. He swallowed, trying to find the right words. He said carelessly, "I hope that we cast no cloud over that visit by our ill-advised urging to have you sing here."

Her steps faltered. "Ill-advised?"

"My wife and I have been talking things over. You are

185

on the threshold of a new career. You must take things gently—not force yourself to clear a hurdle you feel too difficult."

"Too difficult!" There was no mistake now. A note of surprised anger had crept into her voice.

He went on rapidly. "We feel you are wise in your decision not to tempt Providence too far. After all, Garcia's training may have no lasting effect. A breakdown in Stockholm, where you are loved and respected, would not have such serious consequences as a breakdown here."

"Monsieur Bournonville"—she was so angry now, she omitted to call him August—"what in the world makes you think I would have a breakdown here?"

"Well"—he shrugged his shoulders—"you would be singing before an audience much harder to conquer. Besides, The Heiberg comes back to town next week. Look!" His stick pointed to one of the posters. "Everyone will be rushing to hear her. True, it is in a play, but the opera will be neglected. People won't rush to book for a stranger the way they will rush to book for *her*."

Jenny did not reply. The rest of the way home they walked in silence. In silence the luncheon was eaten. After it, Jenny walked into August's private sanctum where he conducted his correspondence. Her head was held high.

"Have you written to the Directors yet?"

"I was just about to do so." He pulled some writing paper hastily toward him.

"Then you may tell them I shall sing in *Robert le Diable*."

A day or two later, new posters sprang out on the walls of Copenhagen. The Swedish Nightingale would make one appearance before her return to Stockholm. Bournonville knew he had exaggerated when he said there would not be enough booking for two great events. There was just as great a run on the tickets for the opera as there was for the theater.

The night came at last. White and tense, Jenny could not swallow any food at all. She allowed Madame Bournonville and Charlotte to dress her. She went down to the carriage on August's arm. They drove together into the enormous square of Kongens Nytorv. Jenny shrank back when she saw the black crowds struggling up the steps of the opera house.

"You told me there would not be many people!" she murmured.

"This is the result of the dress rehearsal yesterday. Don't you remember how everyone cheered you then? How even the cleaners sobbed and clapped? Word has got around. . . ."

She only shivered; felt deadly cold. She knew Hans Andersen would be in the audience, and that cheered her a little. She did not know that Bertil Thorwaldsen, Denmark's world-famous sculptor, would be there too. Thorwaldsen who had lived so long in Italy, who knew the great opera houses there, and who sat in his seat already, waiting to make comparisons.

She changed, mute, into her costume for the First Act. When she stepped into the wings, however, she heard the orchestra playing the Overture, and, as always, she became another person. No longer Jenny, but Alice.

When the time came, she stepped forward fearlessly. The exquisite voice rang out, all-conquering. As Alice, she became part of the story unwinding itself on the stage.

As usual, she did not act her part, she lived it. Nobody there that night stopped to make any comparisons between herself and The Heiberg. She became beautiful, too, but with another sort of beauty; the loveliness of a spirit shining through features nobody bothered to notice were plain. At the end of the First Act, when everyone rose to cheer her, Thorwaldsen rose, too, his handsome bulk visible to everyone who knew him, clapping her to the echo.

By the end of the night she had conquered Copenhagen, just as she had conquered Stockholm long ago.

Hans Andersen stumbled out of the opera house, the tears running down his face. He had seen costly bouquets of flowers lying about her feet. He could not afford to add to them, but he could give her something better—something inspired by herself.

He climbed up the stairs to his lonely room, lit his candle, and began to write. He had already written his famous story of The Nightingale. Now he would write her another, which perhaps only she and he, alone, would understand. She had said herself she was plain, and not like The Heiberg. He had seen her transformed to beauty. He must tell her so, in the only way that he could.

The day before she left Copenhagen, he called on her at the Bournonvilles. After one look at his face, Madame Bournonville excused herself and left them alone.

"Jenny," he said, "take this. And take my heart, too. It belongs to you."

She shook her head sadly. "I will take the envelope, but not the heart. Dear Hans, I love you. Everybody loves you. But I cannot marry you, if that's what you want."

"It is indeed what I want. And yet, how could I expect it? I am poor. I shall always be poor. And I am desperately ugly——"

She put her hand out quickly to stop him. "Do you know me so little? I don't think you ugly, now. At first perhaps, but not now that I have seen your soul. As for your poverty, what does that matter? What does matter is, that I cannot give you the kind of love you want."

"Think it over," he begged. "Read the tale in that envelope when you get back to Sweden. Remember who wrote it. Write and give me some hope—if you can."

Next day the Bournonvilles all went down to the harbor to see her off. There was a crowd there, too, waiting to wave good-by to the Nightingale returning to her own country. But Hans Andersen was not there. He had said his good-by already.

There was an autumn haze over the water. Only the towers of Kronberg Castle stood out to signal farewell. Jenny turned her eyes away from it to gaze in the direction of the Swedish coast now shrouded in mist. A few weeks later and the Sound would be covered with ice. Ships were threading through it swiftly, getting back to England, to Finland, to Sweden, before the great waterway was closed for the winter. Then the ice floes would be blown by the wind toward one shore or the other.

They would clank and jostle against the piers until the wind changed and blew them back to the opposite shore again.

She returned to her northern capital. The Lindbads received her back warmly. Immediately, she was engulfed by the rehearsals for that winter's programme. News of her great success in Copenhagen had already spread through Stockholm, and the whole of Sweden thrilled with pride. After all, what had these Danes to boast about, compared with their Jenny?

Between rehearsals and settling down again, she had scarcely time to breathe. The King and Queen sent for her to congratulate her. They had moved back again to their town palace for the winter. Jenny pulled her fur cape closer to her as she crossed the vast courtyard. The wind had begun to blow cold.

King Karl Johan received her for a moment or two. Although (as he said himself) he was a rough soldier and not a musician, he was proud of the luster she had brought to his country. He spoke a few brief words, and she felt the same sensation of awe and terror with which he had always inspired her. He was not only her King, he had fought with the great Napoleon!

All the same, she thought he looked old and tired. She curtseyed when he had turned to go, and then was led into conversation with the Queen. But it was not the same, sitting here in this vast room, its walls hung with silver-embroidered velvet. Not like Rosendal, where Desideria was herself, a plump, elderly Frenchwoman who had once been pretty.

Now she sat there, plastered with jewels, for there was

to be a Court Ball that evening. "Jean-Baptiste had said all that is necessary by way of compliment," she told Jenny, alluding to her husband in the informal way that made some of her court ladies laugh and some shrug. "And you know, Jenny, how proud and how fond of you I have always been. I want to give you a token of that."

She picked up a small leather case as she spoke. Jenny drew back. "I have your brooch, Your Majesty. Look, I am wearing it now. I want no more."

"Nonsense! Every woman must have jewelry, especially a woman like you, who will appear at other, more splendid Courts than this. My friend the Queen of Hanover is dying to hear you. So are the royalties in Berlin. A starchy lot, and I can't bear the Prussians anyway. But if singing in Berlin will further your career——"

"Your Majesty, please forgive me, but I never intend to leave Sweden again. Never! As for that jewel"—for the Queen had opened the box and a blaze of diamonds almost blinded her—"I have to wear enough paste jewelry on the stage. I would rather, far rather, take the flowers in that vase from your hands."

Reluctantly the Queen closed the box again. She took the flowers out of the vase and handed them to Jenny. The sight of them made her recollect something.

"You put my own flowers on his Tomb?"

"Yes, your Majesty. And I said a little prayer as I dropped them there."

The Queen nodded her head. "I am glad you did that, Protestant as you are. For me, I have never cared to change my religion."

There followed a pause. Jenny ventured to break it by saying: "Does your Majesty mean to attend my opening performance tomorrow night?"

"Of course I do. Let me see, you are singing opposite Belletti are you not? That handsome creature! And I hear he is devoted to you, too."

Jenny showed her dimples. "What tales go around palaces!"

"But you must listen to me, I am serious. Belletti is well spoken of by everyone. He has worshiped you now, for years. Dearest Jenny, I want you to be happy—as happy with a husband as I have been with mine!"

The dimples had gone. Jenny looked grave as she replied, "How can a musician have an ordinary home—ordinary happiness? Forgive me, your Majesty, but with one breath you urge me to go to Hanover and Berlin; with the next to settle down with Belletti! Besides, I am only twenty-three."

Now it was the Queen's turn to smile. "Don't forget I was only fifteen when I was engaged to Napoleon Bonaparte!" She rose, and Jenny immediately rose, too. The Queen kissed her. "Go now, my dear. May happiness come to you someday!"

Jenny was thoughtful as she left the palace. None of the men in love with her seemed to have touched her heart. Or was it, that after expending so much heart in her performances on the stage, she had none left to give anybody?

If she shivered as she crossed the open courtyard again, it was not, this time, from the cold.

Tonight she was not singing. She had her evening

free. Now at last she remembered the envelope given to her by Hans Andersen. She had her supper as usual with the Lindbads. Then she retired early to her room. The envelope lay in a drawer of her desk. She took it out, tore it open, and saw it contained a number of foolscap pages, all covered with Hans Andersen's spidery writing.

A story specially written for her! She looked at the title and for a moment could hardly believe her eyes. Heaven knew, she had always been plain. But had that very plainness inspired him? She read the title twice. It was THE UGLY DUCKLING.

Seated in her comfortable room, with the wood blocks crackling in the stove, she read for the first time the immortal story which has since gone around the world. Of the poor duckling who was chased about by everyone; of its mother who said, "I wish you were miles away." Of the wild ducks who said, "You are appallingly ugly! But why should we care so long as you don't marry into our family?" Until the poor duckling crept into a corner and sat there, feeling very gloomy and depressed.

At this point another thought struck Jenny. Poor Hans is describing himself! He has often told me how people mocked and pushed him aside when he was a boy. And I have seen him sit just like that, when ignorant fashionables who did not know him, turned up to spend the evening at the Bournonvilles!

She began to read on hastily, her heart wrung with pity. All the same, if he was hoping to evoke that pity in order to make her marry him, it was no good! Time passed, in the story. And then the miracle happened.

The duckling grew larger, grew up. The egg he had come from had been placed under the mother-duck to hatch out by mistake. He took to the water and saw his reflection there. He was a beautiful, graceful swan!

"And the old swans bowed to him. . . . He remembered how once he had been despised and persecuted; and now he heard everyone saying that he was the most beautiful of all beautiful birds."

Jenny let the last page fall on her lap. She remembered the awkward, ugly child she had been. She remembered how her mother had pushed her aside in favor of Amalia. But now, Hans Andersen was telling her gently, she was a swan as well as a nightingale.

She dropped some tears on the paper. But they were tears of thankfulness. Presently she roused herself to pick up her pen and write to Hans. She must thank him of course; must tell him how the story had touched her. But she must be careful, too, not to give him any hope. How could she do this best, without seeming ungrateful?

She began with the words, "My dear Brother——"

CHAPTER XIX

In March of the year 1844 a great blow fell on Sweden. Their soldier-king died. Although a foreigner and a Frenchman, he had won their love and respect. When the old line of Swedish kings died out, they had invited him to come and rule over them, and not for one moment had they ever regretted their invitation.

The Crown Prince, Desideria's son, was a handsome young man. No doubt he would make a good king, too. But he had not proved himself as the other had done. The Lion of Sweden went into mourning. The court ladies veiled their white sleeves in black. And the opera house closed for the rest of the season.

"Now Jenny," the Lindbads told her, "now is your chance to go out into the world and win still more fame!"

At last Jenny hesitated. She told herself she need not do what they said. She had not even informed them of the long letter she had received from Berlin, from Hans Andersen. Always a restless wanderer, he had gone there for some distraction. And he had met Meyerbeer, the great composer to whom Jenny had sung in Paris.

Meyerbeer remembered that wonderful voice. He was still working on his new opera. It was nearly finished. It *must* be finished in time for the opening of the new opera house in Berlin. For Meyerbeer was now General Musical Director of the Prussian Court Opera, and he could choose what singers he liked. He wanted Jenny to create the chief rôle in his new opera.

Jenny felt she must really tell Sophie and Adolf about Hans's letter. She showed it to them. They were enthusiastic. "Everyone knows a German audience is the most musical in the world!" they told her, speaking together. Then Adolf went on, "Once sing in Berlin, and you are made!"

Jenny said, "But how can I possibly sing in German? I hardly know a word of the language."

Sophie tried to reassure her. "You can learn any language you like. You have such a quick ear!"

Adolf was already making a plan in his head. "They won't want to put the opera on till next winter. And you are free, now. Why not take a little holiday in Germany, and study the language as well?"

They saw with joy that she was considering it. To sing a whole season in a big capital like Berlin, that was one thing. To spend a few pleasant weeks in a smaller city, that was another. Besides, it was always an advantage to be able to sing an opera in the tongue in which it was written. Hadn't she troubled to learn French, although she had no intention of ever visiting Paris again?

"In Berlin——" Adolf was beginning, when his wife shook her head at him. "Not after all, in Berlin," he amended hastily, "it has a dreadful climate, and is an ugly city as well. But in some place near——"

"In Dresden perhaps?" Sophie suggested. Dresden was not very far from Berlin, and Meyerbeer could easily go there and try to persuade Jenny himself.

That did not strike Jenny. But the thought of

Dresden did. It was a lovely place, she had been told. There were woods and mountains quite near.

"I hear the Dresden Opera House has a remarkable new conductor," she said thoughtfully. "His name is Richard Wagner, I should like to hear him."

Sophie and Adolf nearly clapped their hands. Once get Jenny over the German frontier and who knows what might happen?

So Jenny planned to pack up and go, and take Selma with her. The snow had already melted in the fields around Sollentuna when she drove there to say good-by.

"Well now," said her father, "it's the first time I don't wish to be going with you, Jenny. I don't like German beer. Or German women either. Too fat."

Jenny laughed. She walked out with him into the little garden where the soil was breaking up and the first shoots of plants beginning to show through. In the orchard, the blossom was so white it looked as though the snow had started again. Fru Lind had put her hen coops out into the sun. They could hear the chip-chip of the yellow balls of chicks making their way out of the eggs.

Fru Lind came to the door and threw out some corn for the hens. Jenny, looking at her, saw many of the cross lines smoothed out of her face. With security, and the quiet of the country, her mother had become a much pleasanter person. All the same, she still hankered after more money—if not for herself, then at least for her daughter.

"This German business," she began abruptly, shaking

the last of the corn out of her apron. "What is it going to lead to? Are you going to sing there, Jenny?"

"No, Mother. I told you, I'm going partly for a holiday, partly to learn German."

"A holiday! When the opera house has been closed already for weeks? And what good will learning German do you, if you aren't going to sing in it? But I dare say, once you get there, they'll offer you a handsome fee."

Jenny walked off on her father's arm. It was no use arguing. In her mother's view, nobody went anywhere unless to earn money. But some such thoughts seemed to have visited her father's mind too.

"Listen to me, my girl. You're only getting a pittance from Stockholm now. One hundred and fifty a year. What's one hundred and fifty? Mere—" he glanced back at the coops—"mere chicken feed. That's all."

"Papa!" She gazed up at him reproachfully. "I get paid extra each time I appear, you know that. And the contract has another year to run. I never knew you were mercenary!"

"That's it. That's what I mean. Another year, and they must raise your salary! That is, if you're a success in Germany, and you will be, my dear. Once Stockholm hears of the sensation you'll cause in Berlin, they're bound to try to attract you to stay here!"

She pulled her arm sharply away. "Don't spoil my visit by trying to talk business, Papa. Let's go to the farm and collect Selma. She's gone there to impress them with her new city clothes!"

But for once he was sulky and let her go alone. After he had turned back to the house, she walked slowly past the one that had once been the Ferndals'. It looked neat as ever, and the new sacristan touched his cap respectfully and then bent to his digging again. She glanced up at the tiny window like an eye peeping out of the roof. She remembered how the morning sunshine had poured through the stuff Fru Ferndal had pinned across it, and how it had wakened her, and she had crept downstairs and been taken in charge by Selma. . . .

She took the path over the fields, looking for Selma once more.

A few weeks after this they were off. They had to go by boat to Hamburg, and Selma was seasick. Jenny looked after her, but both were relieved to get on dry land again. They had brought a Swedish newspaper with them, but they had had no time on board ship, to look at it.

Now, seated on their journey across Europe, Jenny handed Selma the paper. Almost at once Selma cried, "Look!" and handed it back.

Her fingers pointed to the lines, "Our beloved Jenny Lind is leaving us. It is believed that she is only traveling to Germany in order to enjoy a well-earned rest. But once the German musical world gets hold of her, it will certainly try to snare our nightingale. When shall we get her back?"

Jenny crumpled the paper up angrily. "How ridiculous!"

Selma said, "I know you mean to go back. But—I must tell you, I didn't like to do so before—they were saying the same thing in Stockholm before we left."

"Saying what? You must tell me, Selma."

"Saying they were going to lose you at the opera house next winter. It is the common talk."

"Look out of the window, dear, and stop chattering nonsense. How neat the houses are in Germany! I wish Papa could see their gardens!"

Selma obediently looked out of the window. And indeed the scene was enchanting. Now they had slipped away from the villages and were plunging through a deep forest. The light struck the barks of the pine trees making them glow a rich red. Never had either of them seen such forests! Jenny thought of her friend Hans Andersen and the enchanting stories he wrote about them. Through the half-opened windows of the carriage they could smell the clean scent of the pines.

At last they reached the city of Dresden. Seated on the banks of the broad River Elbe it had a royal air. The moment they reached their lodgings, Jenny knew she would be happy here.

She found a teacher for German lessons and those kept her busy. But she and Selma had plenty of time, too, to explore. They went down to the river and saw the huge rafts of logs being guided under the bridges. The logs were cut in the forests farther away, then chained together and propelled into the midst of the fast-flowing water until they reached the sawmills farther down.

In the evenings, she would slip quietly into the opera house and watch the performances. She recognized that the standards here were even higher than in Copenhagen and much, much higher than Stockholm's. She watched the new conductor, Herr Wagner, with his mop of hair and his excited gestures. She even heard one of his operas, but she didn't like it.

"I suppose I'm old-fashioned already," she confided to Selma, "but it all seems noise and far too much brass. I like my sweet, melodious Italian operas best."

She visited a few houses, and heard the controversy raging about the new music. Was it just noise, or had it anything in it? Some called Wagner a genius, some a charlatan. The young King of Bavaria was enthusiastic about Wagner's music, she was told. But then people said the King was mad anyway. . . .

One thing everyone was agreed upon. Wagner's operas were very, very long.

Full summer descended upon Dresden. People began to make excursions by boat down the river to get a breath of air. Jenny and Selma went up to the mountains instead. It was an experience, but Selma didn't like it very much, while Jenny decided privately that the scenery was too theatrical, too like the rocks round the Robbers' Cave in some opera set.

"I enjoy myself here, of course," Selma confided to her when they had got back to Dresden, "but I prefer our quiet, flat fields and lakes at home!"

One day a letter arrived with a Berlin postmark. It was from Meyerbeer. If Jenny allowed, might he have the pleasure and privilege of coming to Dresden to see her?

She weighed up the matter. She knew quite well why he wanted to come. He wanted to persuade her to sing in his new opera next winter. The matter didn't look quite the same, now. She knew, now, that Germany

201

ruled the musical world. Her experiences in listening to concerts and opera in Dresden had shown her that. Without appearing in Germany, no singer could count herself in the very first rung.

But then, she must barter her happiness in Sweden for her position abroad! Was it worth it? She talked things over with Selma. The peasant girl had no knowledge of music, but she understood Jenny's feelings. And she had shrewd common sense.

"Tell me, shall I write and say he may come?"

Selma looked at her mistress thoughtfully. "There's no use in a high position if one is unhappy there. Yet, too, one always grudges missing a chance. Also, it is possible to see people without promising anything."

Jenny burst out laughing. "Cautious Selma! Yes of course, he has only asked if he may see me. . . . If he finds he has taken his journey for nothing, that's not my fault."

This evening she was to dine at the house of Herr Kaskel, the Swedish Consul in Dresden. No time to write the letter now; she must dress. . . . The Kaskels lived in a beautiful house a little way out of the city. The River Elbe ran by the bottom of the garden. It would be cool and refreshing. And tomorrow she could write her letter to Meyerbeer. There was plenty of time.

The Kaskels had asked a few friends to meet her. Supper was served on the terrace, with tall candles on the table, and roses strewn carelessly on the white cloth so that their perfume lay on the air. As darkness fell, the lamps on the bows of passing ships shone out as they glided past. It was a fairylike scene.

Most of the other guests were Swedish, too. But as they lingered at the rose-strewn table, Jenny could hear carriages drive up to the door and the guttural sounds of German floating up toward them.

"I have invited a few of our neighbors to join us for coffee," Herr Kaskel explained to her, adding, "I have also been presumptuous enough to promise them that you will sing."

Jenny didn't mind. The warm evening, the delicious meal, the company of her own people, had made her very happy. Although she had firmly intended not to sing once during her holiday, she felt it would be rude to refuse. Besides, why should she, who could give happiness so easily, refuse it to others?

The big drawing room behind the terrace was ablaze with lights. Herr Kaskel's new grand piano stood open, waiting. He led her toward it. Presently her exquisite voice floated out through the open windows, down to the river so that boatmen passing rested on their oars, wondering if some enchantment had fallen upon them. True, the nightingale sings by night. But did any bird sing so sweetly as that?

Herr Kaskel had been very nervous. For years he had heard great reports of Jenny's singing, but as his leave was always in summer when the Stockholm Opera House was closed, he had never heard her himself. And he knew the high standards of his German guests. They had come in a mood of polite criticism. If the Swedish singer was as good as all that, why had she never dared to come and sing in Germany?

Jenny began, as usual, with one or two simple songs of her own country. They touched the hearts of her Swedish listeners, but it was obvious that they also touched the hearts of the Germans. When she had finished, a storm of clapping burst out. But Herr Kaskel was not satisfied. "Well, naturally, she can sing her own songs sympathetically," he could almost hear is German guests whisper to one another," but can she reach the highest flights?"

He was relieved when, after bowing her thanks gracefully, Jenny began to sing one of her operatic arias. Now this was a real test! Her German listeners knew every shake, every *glissade* by heart. They listened critically at first, then with open-mouthed wonder. Never had they heard such perfect, such exquisite, singing in their lives!

When the last note died away, they sat silent. Then they rose and surged toward the piano. "Why have we not heard you sing here, in our Fatherland?" bellowed a fat man in her ear; and the quieter voice of the first music critic in Dresden exclaimed, "*Ach Ja!* Such singing belongs not to Sweden only; it belongs to the world."

Her host managed to extract her from the crowd. Together they stepped onto a balcony overlooking the terrace below. "He is right," the Swede said after a moment. "You must stay here. Such singing does belong to the world."

She knew, humbly, he spoke the truth. It was only what she herself had acknowledged, right from the first. Her voice had been given to her; therefore she must share it with others. Only, she had not thought of the others as living in Germany.

"Herr Meyerbeer wants to come to Dresden to see me," she told him. "I believe he wishes to ask me to sing in his new opera."

His face lit up. "Splendid! Wonderful? I was so proud of you tonight. You showed my German friends that even little Sweden owns one superlative singer. You must show them that too, in Berlin."

She drove back to Dresden along the banks of the river. The moon shone upon it and in the woods, the nightingales sang. For the first time she felt undecided. For the first time she thought: Am I right to refuse to go to Berlin?

Selma was waiting up for her as usual. Often and often she had begged her not to do so. But the little maid was always eager to hear how the evening had gone. Now, as she brushed Jenny's hair, she heard all about it, about the roses lying on the table, the songs and the compliments.

"And Herr Kaskel seems to think it my duty to go to Berlin," Jenny said with a sigh, adding, "it has been lovely here. But oh! I want to go home!"

Selma brushed away in silence. Then she said, "I remember Fru Ferndal once saying, it was the Fates who decided and not oneself."

"I think she meant God. I think He sometimes sends us a sign. Selma, pray tonight that I get a sign from Him tomorrow. I must certainly write to Herr Meyerbeer then."

But Selma wished to see Berlin. She only said, "Maybe

the sign came tonight. Or Herr Meyerbeer will write you another letter tomorrow."

The chambermaid wakened Jenny next morning. She set down the tray of coffee and rolls and pulled back the shutters. "Another lovely day, Fraulein! And there's a letter for you."

Few of her Swedish friends knew where she was. Her parents scarcely ever wrote. So—it must indeed be the letter from Herr Meyerbeer, no doubt saying specifically why he wanted to come.

"The Sign," she said to herself, and picked up the letter that lay on the tray. But it had a Swedish postmark. It had come from Stockholm and looked official. Hurriedly she tore it open. It said, "To announce to Court Singer Jenny Lind that her presence is required in Stockholm immediately, in connection with the special performances at the Royal Theater to celebrate the Coronation of King Oskar I."

So the Sign had come. There was no question that she must obey. She drank her coffee hurriedly, slipped out of bed and scribbled a note of apology to Meyerbeer. She explained that, as she must return to Stockholm, she could not see him. Then she rang her bell for Selma.

"We must pack at once," she told the astonished maid. "We are going back to Sweden."

CHAPTER XX

Stockholm was *en fête* for its new king. Flags were out everywhere and people crowded back to the city before the holiday season was over. The lights of the opera house shone out earlier than usual. There were gala performances, when Jenny sang in two of her best-loved operas, *Norma* and *La Sonnambula,* and everybody crowded as usual, to hear her.

She was glad, and thankful, that Fate had taken matters out of her hands. Here she was at home. She had not the strain of singing to critical strangers. Each night she sang, she could feel the waves of affection and pride in their Jenny coming over the footlights to strengthen her.

One day she had a summons to visit Queen Desideria. The autumn was warm still, and the Queen lingered on in her little pavilion of Rosendal outside Stockholm. Jenny drove through Djorgården, noticing how the slopes of the hills looked withered and brown. The pavilion looked lonely, and the flowers in the porphyry vase were dead.

Desideria sat, a little hunched-up figure in black, on the striped sofa by the glass doors. Her eyes looked as if she had been weeping. She flung her arms around Jenny. "Oh my dear! I have lost Jean-Baptiste. If you had stayed in Germany, I would have lost you, too!"

Jenny sat down beside her, holding her hand. She listened while the dowager queen poured out her sorrow. How kind, how noble, Jean-Baptiste had been. What a devoted husband he had made. "And now," Desideria finished, wiping her eyes, "it remains for my son to carry on his work. At least the Bernadottes have done something for Sweden!"

Jenny was grieved when she had to leave the mourning queen. "You won't leave us again?" Desideria exclaimed, gazing eagerly up at her. "You won't let them tempt you to go to Germany after all?"

Jenny pressed the Queen's hand reassuringly. "I am only happy here. I've found that out. Why should I leave?"

Desideria hesitated. "Remember, I don't exact from you any promise. I mustn't be selfish. But Count Hamilton says——" She broke off suddenly, looking like a frightened child. Jenny wondered. The old Count, the former State Official of the Royal Opera House, was long dead. Count Hamilton reigned in his place.

"Please, your Majesty, what did Count Hamilton say?"

Desideria had put one podgy hand over her mouth. Now, through her fingers she said, "I talk too much. Jean-Baptiste was always saying that. Oh my dear, dear husband! I cannot tell you how much I miss him!"

The tears began to fall again. Jenny kissed them away, then curtseyed and withdrew. But on the long drive home, she could not help wondering what news it was that the queen had so hurriedly suppressed.

A few days later, she got a letter from Berlin, from Meyerbeer. He offered her, definitely, the chief rôle in his new opera. Rehearsals were to start in Berlin in October. The King and Queen of Prussia had promised to be present on the opening night. The opera would stand or fall by the singing of the soprano part.

He begged her to accept it.

If she had once wavered, her joy at being back in Sweden had made her firm again. But, because she had always consulted the Lindbads in everything, she showed them the letter. "I'm not going," she said.

Adolf Lindbad seemed aghast. "It is the chance of a lifetime! And a great honor too. Why, Jenny, you *must* go!"

Sophie's protests were gentler. "I think you are frightened, my dear," she said, "but why should you be?"

"It is *too* great an occasion!" Jenny half-sobbed. "All the Court—all the celebrities will be there. Mendelssohn perhaps, Schumann even. . . . How can I stand up before such an audience and invite comparisons? It is too great a risk. I cannot face it."

Adolf spoke sternly now. "That's just nerves. We've known you all our lives, Sophie and I. Have we ever known you otherwise, on the eve of a great occasion?"

"And I *cannot* leave Sweden. Oh, for a week or two, perhaps. But if I succeed in Berlin, you know what will happen——"

"Of course we know. You will be flooded by invitations to sing all over Europe. Even perhaps, from America——"

"America!" She grew pale at the suggestion. "But there are wild Indians, and people who know nothing about music, and the whole Atlantic to cross!"

"Be quiet, Adolf!" Sophie gave him a warning glance. "That's nonsense, Jenny, and you know it. There are opera houses and musical people in America, too. But of course you don't have to go there. Europe is enough——"

All three were on their feet, arguing. They stood before a tall mirror which ran from the top of the wall to the bottom. In this mirror, Jenny saw the door open. She heard the servant announce, "Count Hamilton."

He was a younger man than the old Count, and a different person altogether. Lazy and nonchalant, people supposed him not a good businessman. But he was, and an enthusiast about music, too. He made an elegant advance toward Jenny.

"Dear Miss Lind! I have a trifle of business to talk over with you. . . . Your servant, Fru Lindbad. How do, Adolf?"

The Lindbads prepared to retire. Jenny stopped them. "Please stay. I have always consulted you about my business. I should like the Count to state it before us all."

The Count bowed, cleared his throat. "Your old contract has run out, as you know. The Directors have empowered me to offer you another. It is of an unusual nature—unusually generous, you will agree. To begin with, we propose to raise your salary to five thousand *Riksdalers* a year."

"Five thousand *Riksdalers!*" Jenny felt stunned. It was far, far above anything anyone had been offered by the Stockholm Directors before. Swiftly she thought of all the good she could do with so much money. There was Louise Johanson—now she could set her up in a shop of her own! She could increase her allowance to Papa and Mama! She could——"

"You said, to begin with?" Adolf Lindbad interjected.

"Ah yes. This is the unusual part of the contract. Indeed, it is quite exceptional. We offer this sum, not only for the years the contract runs, but forever! At the close of the term stated, should you wish to retire (but I hope not, I hope not) you may still draw five thousand *Riksdalers* for the rest of your life!"

Security for the rest of her life! Even if her voice failed once more . . . Jenny was just about to accept the offer gratefully, when Lindbad interrupted again.

"Your Excellency has not told us how long the contract is to run."

"Ah no, I forgot that. H'm. It says here, 'for a period of eight years.' " He laid the stiff paper on the table before Jenny as he spoke.

"Eight years!"

"No time at all, when one considers Mademoiselle's present age. She is only twenty-four now, is she not? But of course"—the Count tapped the contract with his manicured forefinger as he spoke—"this will preclude any appearances elsewhere—during the opera season at least."

Adolf picked up the contract quickly. "May I speak for you, Jenny?" He turned to the Count. "She will read this carefully, and do some thinking, and let you know."

"By all means! By all means! Shall we say, in three

211

days' time? My Directors would like her signature as soon as possible."

When the Count had gone, Adolf said: "Do you see what this means? They've had wind of your offer from Berlin. They don't want to lose you. So they are trying to tie you down for an absurd length of time—for eight years!"

Jenny answered him hotly. "Why did you stop me signing? All I can see is that for eight years I can have the pleasure of remaining in my own country, among my own friends; and be handsomely paid for it, too!"

"Oh Jenny! I know you want money, not for yourself but to give for others. Have you ever considered the fortune you would be paid abroad? Our little country simply could not compete!"

But she shook her head obstinately. In vain both Sophie and Adolf pleaded with her. The most they could wring from her was a promise to keep the contract unsigned, for the three days the Count had allowed. Adolf was so heated, he forgot that the letter from Meyerbeer must be answered, too. It was Sophie who remembered.

"Jenny dear, I know you don't like to refuse me anything. You have promised Adolf that at least you won't sign the new contract for three days. Will you promise me that you won't write to Herr Meyerbeer till then, too?"

"Of course I'll promise you that. But all the same, at the end of three days, I shall write to refuse his offer."

She went to Sollentuna next day. She wanted to be out of the way of the Lindbads' pleading. Besides, she must see her parents while the roads were still open and before the snow came. The little village looked beautiful in the calm autumn weather. Fru Lind's chicks had grown up. They came rushing to Jenny, wings outstretched, in the hope of some food.

Niclas Lind had caught some fish. His wife had pounded them raw, made them into balls and dipped them in egg batter. Then she fried them for midday dinner. They were delicious. Jenny had brought some coffee beans from the city. They roasted in the oven while the meal was being eaten. Then Fru Lind put them into the coffee grinder she had inherited from her mother. Presently the little house was full of the fragrance of coffee.

While they sipped it, Jenny told them her news.

"Five thousand *Riksdalers!*" Niclas threw up his hands in astonishment. "Why, you will be a rich woman, Jenny! Now then. What about a new gun for me to go duck shooting?"

"And for the rest of her life!" Fru Lind's tone sounded resentful. "Just for opening her mouth. Some people have all the luck!"

Jenny promised her father the new gun. There were so many other delightful things she could do now, once the contract was signed! It was late when she drove back to the city. The sky was a greenish color, and the Northern Dancers flickered on the horizon.

She stole quietly into the Lindbads' house, and crept past the sitting-room doors until she reached the safety of her own bedroom. She wanted no more argument. Especially, she wanted no quarrel with her best friends.

213

Later, when she was safely in bed, Sophie tapped on her door and looked in. But she lay with her eyes closed, pretending to be asleep.

So the first day passed. On the morning of the second, Jenny got up early and again left the house before she could be intercepted. She went to her practicing-room at the opera, and ran over the score of the next opera to be given there. She sent a message to the Lindbads that she would not be back for lunch, she was lunching with friends.

"She's keeping out of our way," said Adolf when the message came.

Sophie said, "Poor child! If we plead with her more, she will only be more unhappy. She's unhappy now, at having withstood us about anything. We can't move her, that's clear. We must leave her now, to her own decision."

"But if it's a bad one?" Adolf snapped.

"We've said everything. What more is there left to say?"

"I love Jenny, but sometimes I could wring her neck. Sheer obstinacy, that's all it is. I'm going out for a walk."

He stumped along the street muttering sheer obstinacy, sheer obstinacy, to himself. Of course he and Sophie would miss her—miss her dreadfully, if she went abroad. But if they felt they had no right to keep her genius from the rest of the world, why couldn't she feel the same?

He bumped into a broad, elderly figure without noticing. A voice with a guttural German accent exclaimed, "Why, Herr Lindbad? What has upset you so that you nearly knock down your friends?"

It was the German Consul-General. Lindbad found the old man tiresome. He was so full of his own opinions; so sure nobody had any musical taste but himself and his German friends! But Adolf had reached the stage when he had to confide in somebody. As they walked along together, he poured out the story of Meyerbeer's offer, and Jenny's determination not to accept it.

"Eh, Eh? So Meyerbeer has actually offered such a part to an untried singer? I am amazed."

Adolf was so astonished by the remark, he stopped dead on the pavement. "Untried? Did you say untried? Why, Jenny has sung all the great rôles here in Stockholm, for nearly ten years——"

"*Ach so.* In Stockholm! But what is Stockholm, *Mein Freund*, compared with Berlin? Yes, the little Jenny is wise. She knows she is not up to our standard in Germany. In that, she shows sense."

Adolf stared at the German, speechless. For a moment he was too angry to utter a word. The Consul-General gazed back at him, looking self-satisfied. "We have the finest singers in the world," he was saying. "And the finest, most cultured audiences, too. What will pass here in Stockholm, won't pass there, I assure you!"

Still speechless, Adolf flung angrily away. But the old man's chuckle was still in his ears. Obstinate devils, those Germans! he told himself in his rage. Obstinate! Obstinate! . . .

Suddenly he stood stock still. Then he began to hurry

back home, almost running. . . . as fast as he could.

He leaped up his own staircase two steps at a time; then made himself slow down, so that he could enter the drawing room casually. He knew Jenny was there. She was playing on the piano, trying over one of his own songs in a sweet half-voice. He opened the door and walked in. Sophie was there, too, working at her embroidery. Jenny was obviously making music to stop any conversation.

She went on playing, until he lifted the contract off the table, where it had lain ever since the Count had flung it down. When she saw him do this, she stopped.

"My dear," he said, "the sooner this thing is signed, the better."

Both women stared at him, astonished. He went on rapidly. "By chance I met the German Consul-General, half an hour ago. He is a great connoisseur of singing, as you know. He advises you not to accept Meyerbeer's invitation."

"Not to accept——" Jenny had risen from the piano stool and was gazing at him in still greater astonishment.

"He thinks you are right not to challenge a Berlin audience."

Jenny walked slowly towards him and took the contract out of his hand. "Why did he say that?"

"Well—he thinks you are not quite up to its standards."

"Adolf!" Sophie sounded as if she thought her husband had gone out of his mind. "What a thing to say to our Jenny! How unkind and untrue! You know as well

216

as I, that she is the idol of Stockholm!"

Jenny was standing now before the great mirror, the contract still in her hand. They could only see her back, but that was as stiff as a ramrod. Adolf swallowed, then forced his voice to sound natural, kindly, regretful.

"That's the trouble. What does Stockholm count, or even Copenhagen for that matter? We must not press her any more, Sophie. Anyone—even our Nightingale—would flinch before Berlin!"

The figure in the white dress still stared into the mirror. Adolf held his breath. What was Jenny seeing there? Was she seeing into the future, when she would conquer Berlin and the whole of Germany—the whole of the world?

The figure whirled round suddenly. Jenny's face was as white as her dress. With trembling fingers she tore the contract across, and again across. She threw the bits of paper on the floor.

"I will go to Berlin!"

Finale

And what happened to Jenny afterward?

Her visit to Berlin was electrifying. At her first night, the German audience, the most musical and most disciplined audience in the world, actually halted the opera with its roars of applause, forcing Jenny to sing the chief aria over again. She was summoned to Court and presented with valuable jewels. But she valued far more the meeting and friendship with Felix Mendelssohn.

They had met, that year, at a party in Berlin. They understood one another from the first. The handsome, sympathetic composer and the great singer made a wonderful team, for now Jenny began to include Mendelssohn's songs in her concert programmes. On his death, she found she could not sing his songs in public any more. Her remembrances of him, and her sorrow, were too great.

But she still had his friendship and support while she took the next steps in her fantastic career. From Berlin she went to Vienna, where the audience refused to leave the opera house after the curtain came down. Outside it, a vast crowd gathered, waiting to see Jenny leave. She was imprisoned behind the scenes for hours, and when at last she had to venture out, the mob surrounded her carriage and she had to be rescued by mounted police.

It was Mendelssohn who encouraged her to sing the

songs of Schumann and Schubert as well as his own. He interested her in Oratorio, for he had been working on his *Elijah*. And it was he who helped to persuade her to come to London at last—though Jenny had said she would never go there.

But in the year 1847 she did. Her success in opera repeated itself—there was nothing strange about that. Queen Victoria, who knew and admired Mendelssohn, and who was a good amateur musician herself, expressed her enthusiasm to the Manager of the opera house in a way he had never heard her speak of any singer before. She presented Jenny with a diamond Nightingale to wear in her hair. One night, when Parliament was sitting, it had to be dismissed because there were too few members present to carry out anything. More than half the government of the country was at the opera, listening to the Nightingale sing.

All sorts of goods in the London shops, from bonnets to flat-irons, were called after her. There was a popular song, whistled in the streets or sung in the music halls, which said:

> *Oh! Is there not a pretty fuss*
> *In London all around,*
> *About the Swedish Nightingale,*
> *The talk of all the town?*
>
> *Now everything is Jenny Lind*
> *That comes out each new day,*
> *There's Jenny Lind shawls and bonnets too,*
> *For those who cash can pay. . . .*

None of this was specially strange. But what *was* strange, was that Jenny found herself more at home in England than anywhere else. She liked the quiet, restrained English people who did not embarrass her by fussing over her in her private life. She liked the English landscape and the English ways. She rented a pretty house called Clairville Cottage, and had her old friend Louise Johanson staying with her there as well as her old playmate Selma. For she had soon rescued Louise from her dressmaking, and had made her her companion instead. Louise was to find the constant traveling too hard. She left Jenny soon afterward. But the friends always kept in touch, and Jenny remembered both her and her faithful maid in her Will.

It was during that visit to England, on one of the occasions when Queen Victoria entertained her privately as an admiring friend, that Jenny first confessed her new longing to leave the stage. More and more, she wanted to sing in oratorio, or to sing sacred songs only. She had always been a religious-minded girl. Now her religious feelings had deepened until she had almost come to believe, with her mother and her old grandmother, that there was something wrong about singing on the stage.

But she did not take that decisive step yet. She went back on a visit to Sweden. Her own people greeted her with wild delight. She gave every penny of her performances during that winter's season, to establish a fund for orphan children of the Opera School. She sang for many other charities too. The year 1848 saw her once more in London, filling the opera house and enchanting everyone. She gave away so much to charity, that she could not afford yet, to please herself about the sort of music she wished to sing.

It was about this time that Phineas Barnum, the great American Showman, began to have hankerings after culture. He said so frankly in his memoirs. "Inasmuch as my name had long been associated with 'humbug,' and the American public suspected my capacities did not extend beyond the power to exhibit a stuffed monkey, I could afford to lose $50,000 in bringing to this country, in the zenith of her life and celebrity, the greatest musical wonder in the world."

But The Swedish Nightingale was not easily snared. For long she refused even to consider his offers which he steadily increased until he finally promised the sum of $150,000—a much larger amount in these days than now —for a stated number of concerts. Jenny finally agreed to go—she had become curious to see the great continent which once she had feared. Her visit to America was so successful she stayed for two years. It was here that her greatest happiness came to her. A young German pianist, Otto Goldschmidt, came over from Europe to act as her accompanist. He had been recommended to her by Felix Mendelssohn years ago. Now, with this link of friendship between them, she found herself leaning on Otto's quiet strength more and more. Not only did he accompany her exquisitely, but he gave her wise guidance and gentle support.

There came a day when the words of her old friend Belletti came back to her with new meaning. *You will fall in love someday. You cannot awake so much love without returning it too.* It had happened, and she knew her love was returned.

In 1852 she and Otto were married. Jenny's loneliness was over at last. But for some time her wandering life continued. When she finally gave up the stage, she had turned more and more to singing in Oratorio, and England was the home of Oratorio. It was the home, besides, of her great friend and admirer, Queen Victoria. And the climate suited Otto and the children. . . .

So, instead of finally returning to Sweden, she and her little family settled down in England after all. Otto said he found there the peace he needed in order to compose and teach. He became Professor of Piano at the Royal Academy of Music in London, and soon after was made Vice-President of the Academy. But Jenny never forgot her native land and paid it frequent visits. She founded three scholarships for Swedish students; but the old dream of settling down there had somehow vanished.

Presently her golden career began to draw to its close. She had left the footlights long ago. Her chief appearances for many years had been in such works as Haydn's *Creation* or the *Elijah* of her great and dearest friend, Mendelssohn. Now the glorious voice was beginning to fail. But if she could do nothing else, she could teach.

So the Nightingale became, in 1883, First Professor of Singing at the Royal College of Music which had just been opened in London. In 1886 she was forced to resign from ill health. Next year, in the autumn, she died. She was buried where her last days were spent, at Great Malvern. They laid beside her, as she herself wished, a patchwork quilt made and given to her by the children of America long ago; that, and an Indian shawl Queen Victoria had given her. Over her grave they placed a simple stone of Swedish granite. And her Memorial can be seen in Westminster Abbey.

But it was King Oscar II of Sweden—the great-grandson of Jenny's old friend Queen Desideria—who said the last words about Jenny Lind when he heard of her death. "She was like a meteor, blazing its trail above the heads of a wondering world."

BOOKS FOR FURTHER READING

Benét, Laura, THE ENCHANTING JENNY LIND. New York, Dodd, Mead and Co., 1939.

Bök, Fredrick, HANS CHRISTIAN ANDERSEN: A BIOGRAPHY. University of Oklahoma Press, 1962.

Godden, Rumer, HANS CHRISTIAN ANDERSEN. New York, Alfred A. Knopf, Inc., 1955.

Barnum, P. T., P. T. BARNUM'S OWN STORY. Waldo R. Browne, ed. Gloucester, Massachusetts, Peter Smith, 1962. (This title is also available in a paperback edition—New York, Dover Publications, Inc., 1961)

Wallace, Irving, FABULOUS SHOWMAN: THE LIFE AND TIMES OF P. T. BARNUM. New York, Alfred A. Knopf, Inc., 1959.

Wells, Helen, BARNUM: SHOWMAN OF AMERICA. New York, David McKay Co., Inc., 1957.

Bruhn, Erik and Moore, Lillian, BOURNONVILLE AND BALLET TECHNIQUE. New York, The Macmillan Company, 1961.

Selinko, Annemarie, DÉSIRÉE. New York, William Morrow and Co., Inc., 1953.

Erskine, John, SONG WITHOUT WORDS: THE STORY OF FELIX MENDELSSOHN. New York, Julian Messner, Inc., 1942.